The
long lost
manuscript
of
Lou Beach

No City For Dreaming

as edited by Don O'Melveny

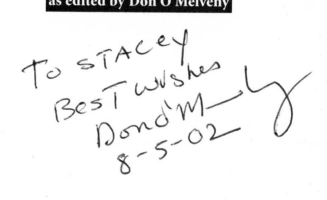

To STACey
BesT wishes
DondM——y
8-5-02

sanyata

PUBLISHING

LIBRARY OF CONGRESS CATALOGING IN PUBLICATION DATA

O'Melveny, Don
        No City For Dreaming.

        1. Title.

ISBN 0-9721808-0-X

Library of Congress Control Number: 2002092769

Deepest thanks to
Joan and Hank, Soon,
Michael E., Edem,
Heather and Mazin.

Prologue

The publishers have asked me, Don O'Melveny, to give a brief account of the events that brought about the discovery of this extraordinary, long-missing manuscript and the ultimate unveiling of perhaps Los Angeles' most infamously unsolved murder. I'm referring to the mysterious and never fully explained circumstances surrounding Marilyn Monroe's death - a death that has persistently haunted the American psyche since that August night some forty years ago.

Year after year her presence remains with us – through books, movies, photo collections, fan clubs, look-a-like contests, along with the undercurrents of rumors and speculation. Ethereally floating through our collective unconscious, trickling into us like an opiate, it is as if some part of us has never fully been satisfied by the official explanation of "accidental overdose" and we continue to hunger for the real truth. And it is precisely because her death has never fully and truthfully been explained that she continues to haunt us – until it is. However, I am not here to substantiate or further the incriminating facts and unexplained circumstances. Thankfully, others have already done that in sufficient evidence. My task is to provide the reader a factual account of the screenplay's discovery and authenticity, some background on the author of this remarkable story, why it took so long to surface, and finally how it came into my possession.

First of all, I should warn the reader this is no lurid, tell-all expose. It is the creative re-telling of the author, Lou Beach's, first-hand account of his direct involvement in events surrounding Marilyn's last days, and his uncovering of the participants in the elaborately designed murder conspiracy. Why screenplay? Beach, at the time, was in fact a screenwriter – somewhat struggling to break into the industry but employed as an investigator. Given this, I don't think it surprising he chose the screenplay as his medium of expression when it came time for him to tell his tale. To those who have never read a screenplay – don't be put off. This is a page-turner, highly literate and immensely readable. However, if one is solely looking for sensationalism or titillating details, there will likely be disappointment. As a screenwriter, he has allowed himself a fuller canvas, to get a larger truth than the mere factual assemblage of a traditional non-fiction account. To call this a Marilyn script would be like calling, say – the movie CHINATOWN a story just about Mulholland. As the title suggests, it is a story about a city – as much about Hollywood and the primordial mind-set it engenders as about Marilyn or the author.

Given all this, there is a tangible appropriateness to having this of all stories surface as a screenplay – a certain poetic logic, perhaps even justice, for this noir, seductive, epic Hollywood insider's saga to be revealed within the pages of a screenplay.

But perhaps I am getting ahead of myself. Let me return to the facts as they are. I run a gallery in West Hollywood for modern, contemporary art. It was in March of 1996 that there was to be a large charity auction in Pasadena, with many items coming from my late Uncle's personal estate. My Chinese girlfriend Zhen was excited about attending. I deferred, with a golf date I had no intention of breaking. I should mention my late uncle was the last acting O'Melveny to head the family law firm of O'Melveny and Myers, which was founded by my great grandfather Henry O'Melveny in 1889, and is considered to be the oldest and most prestigious firm in the city. And, in fact, Uncle Jack figures peripherally in the story.

At any rate, a large number of my uncle's possessions were donated for the auction, and Zhen thought it important to acquire a few items – possibly of some historical significance and certainly for some emotional value. She had her heart set on Bing Crosby's ukulele from the film ROAD TO BALI the old crooner had presented my uncle with. She was outbid and had to settle for a very handsome desk-size set of reference books, a smoking jacket, and a small California impressionist painting. I was pleased for her, but hardly impressed when she showed me her acquisitions during a cocktail before dinner. But, as I was re-checking my golf score, she screamed: "Oh, my God! What's this?"

It seems a card had slipped from one of the pages of the small volumes. She read it again, then handed it to me, saying: "I think this might be something." I inspected. It appeared to be a combination to a safety deposit box, written on the back of an old, faded Wells Fargo bank card. Also the name – LOU BEACH.

"Oh, come on, honey – you don't really think --- ?"

She did, and the next day proved her right. We went to the bank and after presenting the proper family identification and relating the special circumstances, were allowed into the security room. And there, in 2011-A, lay a simple, battered, but well-preserved stationery box. And inside, neatly nestled, lay the manuscript – some 145 pages of Southwest 20 lb. bond ivory-white typing paper.

Both Zhen and I looked at each other, not sure exactly what to think – or what the pages might represent, but took the stationery box home with us. Later at the gallery, I received a call from Zhen.

"You won't believe what this is," she nearly screamed.

"Calm down for goodness sake – what is --?"

"The manuscript. I guess it's a movie script. But it's - remarkable!"

I had thought it might simply be some old misplaced legal work for which my uncle could have forgotten about during the course of a long and distinguished career.

"You're saying it's a book -- ? I wondered, "....that he wrote a screenplay?"

"No. Not your uncle. Someone named Lou Beach. The name on the back of the card."

The Beach name was of course familiar to me, belonging to one of L.A.'s oldest families, and long-time friends with the O'Melveny's. In fact, Michael Beach is a close friend of mine.

"You've got to read this," Zhen insisted.

"What kind of story is it?" I asked.

"Non-fiction. Fiction. Memoir. I'm not sure. But I'm sitting here, reading it, page after page – and I'm shaking!"

As I did, later that evening, staying up well into the night to finish the extraordinary telling.

Nothing less than stunned, I resolved to take a few days off so that Zhen and I could piece together the particulars behind the manuscript and how it came into my uncle's possession. And, if we could somehow validate the manuscript's substance, we wanted to seek its publication.

In the summer of 1962, Lou Beach, 29, was working as an investigator for my uncle Jack at O'Melveny and Myers. As I've said, the families were friends and explains how Beach came to be working there. This, however, was not Beach's true ambition. For six years prior, upon graduating from UC Berkeley, he had pursued a writing career. To his great disappointment I'm sure, this ambition was not met with any substantial success – and after six years of the struggling writer's meager and disillusioned life, he stowed away his Smith-Corona and began poking around for a more sensible career, one certainly with a better financial future. Among the prospects was the opportunity to enter his family's long-estab-lished and highly regarded investment firm, Nicholas Beach, Inc. It was during this time of working for O'Melveny and pondering his future that it all happened. The story of those five days in August, 1962.

Due to conditions that will be plainly evident in the story's unfoldment, Beach was forced to leave Los Angeles, fleeing it seems to Mexico – and later into the heart of Asia. And while he has never presumably returned, sometime in the late 60's he did send my uncle the manuscript, knowing a part of the O'Melveny practice dealt in entertainment, and hopeful a publisher might be secured.

From what I've gathered, it seems my uncle did try, but was told the manuscript – dealing as it did with the Monroe/Kennedys' romance, was far too sensitive to risk publishing. It seems likely my uncle, ever an advocate of the conservative path, favored a "let sleeping dogs lie" attitude and allowed the manuscript to settle into obscurity. Out of sight, out of mind. And with my uncle's retirement in the mid-seventies, it all but sealed the forgotten manuscript's fate to its dark, security-box entombment.

Of Beach, I know precious little. Over the years, Michael informed me, there were occasional postcards and letters, providing a very sketchy profile. It is known he studied in a Buddhist's retreat outside Kyoto, trained and worked as a chef, drank with Graham Greene in Bangkok, taught English literature in Singapore, did some voice-over work in Taipei and enjoyed a certain amount of success as a free-lance journalist. In other words, he had a life. A rather good one, if I'm not mistaken.

But the family had no idea whatsoever about the manuscript. Indeed, there are strong reasons of a security nature that cautioned Beach to minimize his family's involvement. And, in fact, they insisted for publication their name be changed and identities safely disguised. I can say this, that with the book's publication, I'm anxious to see if this brings Beach back to the surface. Aside from the recognition and royalties, I'd relish simply sitting down with him for an evening's worth of stories from what has to have been an exotically textured life abroad.

This was all well and good, but there remained for Zhen and I a lingering sense of unfinished business. We wanted something of proof, validating all that Beach describes actually did happen. We did not want readers skeptically thinking it was all a very skillful rendering of events under the guise of authenticity. Playing devil's advocate, Zhen argued it didn't necessarily matter because the Kennedy/Monroe part was largely background – a historical canvass intersecting with Beach and the beautiful struggling Asian actress. The macro for the micro. I, on the other hand, felt if such proof did exist, something of indisputable validation, it would remove all doubt and squelch any rumors of some finely wrought Wellesian façade.

And as luck would have it, such an artifact did exist, coming from a most unlikely but equally respected source – beginning with an acquisition from the famous Jackie Onassis auction at Sotheby's in 1996. Tempted as I am to include this now – as it led Zhen and I on our own small odyssey of discovery and a final, truly shocking revelation, the publishers feel it belongs in a concluding, epilogue section.

So without further delay, I now present NO CITY FOR DREAMING – the long-lost screenplay of Lou Beach.

Hollywood August 3, 1962

EXT. A BAR ON WILSHIRE BLVD.   EVENING

The name of the bar is SWAMIS, an old-fashioned place on the eastern fringe of Beverly Hills. A closed-down movie theater neighbors Swamis.

ANGLE ON SIDEWALK on a young guy, waiting anxiously – looking up and down Wilshire, at the cars passing. The SWAMIS NEON SIGN comes on – a golden amber, beckoning. He checks his watch.

ANOTHER ANGLE as a black car pulls up and stops. The guy, we'll call him THE PROJECTIONIST, runs up to the passenger window. An arm comes out, extending a flat box – that looks like it could contain a film reel. The projectionist takes and splits inside Swamis.

INT.   SWAMIS   SAME

A really cool, divey kind of place. Vintage noir. A place for guys between pictures to wait with languid style.. The projectionist hustles down the long bar for the rear.

> BARTENDER
> (to projectionist)
> They're waiting. Had two drinks.

We follow the projectionist to a rear side door that connects to

INT.   THEATER   SAME

The adjoining theater. The projectionist enters and continues to stairs leading up to the projection booth.

ANOTHER ANGLE of two men – the only ones in the place, seated, waiting, nursing a couple drinks.

ON THE PROJECTIONIST as he enters the booth and nimbly opens the case, removes a reel of film, and begins threading it into the projector.

PROJECTIONIST
(to the guys below)
Give me just a second.

BACK ON THE TWO GUYS as they continue nursing their drinks, chatting.
The Texan is BOOTS, fifty-ish, his attire unfailingly western, especially the
boots. The other is NEAL, same age, tall and handsome in a Robert Mitchum
kind of way.

NEAL
So what do you think about Drysdale.
Will he get number 100 tonight against
The Giants?

BOOTS
(Texan drawl)
I ain't a Dodger fan. Ain't a
Movie fan. Most actors are self-
Absorbed ass-holes. My idea of music
Ain't a bunch of high school kids
Singing about surfin'…But I tell
You what I would appreciate knowin'.

NEAL
What's that Boots?

BOOTS
Where an ol' Texan can get
Himself some real god-damn bar-b-que!?
You're a cop --- cops know 'bout food,
don't they, Neal? Been here two years
and still haven't found anything close.

NEAL
(smiling)
What kind you looking for –
Shit-kicking or fire code red?

                           BOOTS
                   Kind I can smell cookin'
                   Couple blocks away.

The LIGHTS dim down.

                        PROJECTIONIST (OS)
                   Show time.

                           BOOTS
                   Speakin' of bar-b-quein...
                        (nods toward the screen)
                   did I tell you the kids name –
                   it's Lou Beach.

Neal nods, and the two men settle in, facing the screen as

A SHEATH OF LIGHT hits the screen. Black and white, home movie
quality FOOTAGE:

What we see is waves breaking, Malibu, by the pier. A warm summer day.
Specifically we are watching a cluster of SURFERS paddling for a wave.

CAMERA ZOOMS IN ON

SURFER catching the wave before others and angling down the six footer.
Dark-haired, 29-ish, ruggedly handsome, he is LOU BEACH.

                           NEAL (OS)
                   That him?

                           BOOTS (OS)
                   Yep, the Kid. The one.

The surfer, Lou, is good. Definitely knows what he's doing.

                          NEAL (OS)
Not so much a kid.

                          BOOTS (OS)
Trust me, he's a kid. And he's
Exactly what we want.

                            NEAL
Tell me.

                           BOOTS
Grandson of Nicholas Beach. Raised
In Pasadena. Graduated UC Berkeley '54.

The waves takes Lou into shore. He walks out, carrying his board.

                           BOOTS
None of which really matters. Except
The family has kind of dis-owned him.

                            NEAL
Why's that?

                           BOOTS
Pretty much a fuck-up in their
Eyes. Shined on the family business –
Investments. Thinks he's a writer.
Lives in Hollywood. Which is a major
No–no for those blue-bloods.

Staying with Lou, the footage shows him moving up the beach to a spot in
front of a row of parked cars. He sets his board down, grabs a towel, and
dries off.

                           BOOTS
He even goes to one of those
Friggin' oriental churches…
Y'know where they sit on the floor

                             10

BOOTS (CONT'D)
And mumble a bunch of shit. He's
Definitely wired weird.

NEAL
Some kind of cult thing?

BOOTS
Who knows. But we can use later.
When the shit hits the fan.

NEAL
Good So he's out's with the family
What else?

CONTINUING WITH FOOTAGE - Lou grabs a drink from his car, sets a
chair down on the sand, sitting down with a pad of legal paper and pencil.

BOOTS
He's soft. Will do what he's told.
We can maneuver him, no prob.

NEAL
Who got him into Kennedy land?

BOOTS
Can't cough that up.

NEAL
So how do we know he'll take the gig?

BOOTS
"Cause he's a crazy, fucked up writer
and he'll smell story. A story too good to
pass. He's just like all the other
dumb fucks struggling in this town - waiting
for the phone to ring with their big break.

Lou turns, putting on sun-glasses. He swings his glance so he is staring now right into the camera. His gaze holds, almost as if he has spotted the camera. But he does nothing. Start to GO IN on Lou.

> BOOTS
> He's got the bug. The Hollywood
> Bug. And he's got it bad.

FREEZE ON LOU

> BOOTS
> (to projection guy)
> Mark that one. For a print.

The film turns OFF – leaving the theater and the two men in DARKNESS.

> NEAL
> By the way, I'm going to need an extra
> Fifty G's.

> BOOTS
> Why's that?

> NEAL
> Gotta fix the coroner.

STAY DARK for a beat then we go to

EXT. HOLLYWOOD BOULEVARD EARLY EVENING

CLOSE ANGLE ON THE STARS of the famed boulevard. CAMERA MOVES along the pavement. As the stars of the famous Hollywood celebrities pass, we begin to get the feeling we are following behind a particular pair of feet – distinctly feminine. We don't know who, but that doesn't matter now. It's just the feeling of walking and the stars and the whole Hollywood feeling we want.

ANGLE ON YOUNG WOMAN – the one we've been following. CHERIE WINTERS, blonde, early twenties, a bit uncared for, but also strikingly beautiful if you look carefully. She has on a short skirt, fishnet stockings. Her blouse reveals nice cleavage. And there is an unmistakable sexy quality to Cherie.

ANOTHER ANGLE as she continues her course along the boulevard. She isn't just idly walking but is actually absorbed in a script – rehearsing lines out lout – oblivious to the stares of those around her. During her lines, we detect a slight trace of an accent, though her appearance doesn't help us identify it.

CLOSE ON CHERIE as she finishes hr lines and smiles – really pleased with herself. Whatever she was trying for, she seems to have nailed it. She hugs her script, confident and happy.

ON DOOR behind her, reading: SY MACK PRODUCTIONS. There is a small sheet that reads: BACK ALLEY GIRL CASTING.

ON CHERIE feeling a small, delicate star-shaped pendant around her neck.

CHERIE
(for luck)
I can do it. I can. I am going
To do it!

And we feel, whatever it is – getting the part, she will succeed. Her prayer offered, she opens the door and enters.

INT.   SY MACK PRODUCTIONS   SAME

Cherie is quickly greeted by a guy with a clipboard. There is a long line of girls waiting on the other side of this guy. He asks who she is.

CHERIE
Cherie Winters.

The guy looks down the list of names on his clipboard. But can't find it.

CHERIE

But it has to be.

GUY

It's not here. Sorry.

She protests again, but to no avail. The guy's not letting her in. He allows her
to use a phone to call her agent.

CHERIE

Drew – it's Cherie. At the Sy Mack
Audition. Something's wrong – they
Say I'm not on the list.

DREW (agent)

Sorry, doll. Things are a little slow
These days. I gotta trim down. Focus
On my A list.

CHERIE

What -- ?!?

DREW

I gotta drop you, kid. Sorry.

CHERIE

From the picture ---?!?

DREW

(sharper)
From the Agency. I can't represent you
Anymore. G'Bye!

She tries to catch him, but he's gone. She slowly hangs up. Hold on her,
SIGHING with a hurting disappointment as we go to

EXT.   DOWNTOWN   EVENING

EST. shot of the CALIFORNIA CLUB

INT.   PRIVATE ROOM

We're with Attorney JACK O'MELVENY and the surfer we saw earlier at
Malibu. LOU BEACH. Lou is standing while a tailor is taking his measure-
ments. Holding his arms outright, Lou complies, allowing the tailor to
move/adjust his body position to get the measurement.

> O'MELVENY
> Fifty thousand to start. Review after
> Ninety days. Most like a bump up.
> Company car. Two weeks paid vacation.
> Some other perks.

Lou nods, somewhat pleased. O'Melveny places the contract on the table
beside them. Lou looks down at it, while the tailor continues.

> O'MELVENY
> It's a good offer, Lou. Your father's
> Being more than generous. He really
> Wants you to come aboard.

> BEACH
> When would I start?

> O'MELVENY
> Straight away. He'd like to announce it
> At your grandfather's retirement   party
> Saturday night.

> BEACH
> He wants to announce it?

> O'MELVENY
> It'll be perfect – with everyone there. A big moment   for
> the family. Changing of the guards.

15

Lou nods, getting the drift.

> O'MELVENY
> There is one proviso. That you stow away
> the Smith-Corona!

> BEACH
> Stop writing --?!

> O'MELVENY
> (nodding)
> For good. And give your full,
> Undivided attention to the family firm.

Lou SIGHS, pulling a hand through his hair. This is tough. The tailor shifts
him around, spreading his legs apart.

> O'MELVENY
> Lou – for Christ's sake! It's
> For your own good. You're
> Nearly thirty. It's time, kiddo,
> To get on with your life.
> Working for me as a legal snoop is interim at best.
> And for Pete's sake - move back to Pasadena.
> Nobody lives in Hollywood.

> BEACH
> I like it.

> O'MELVENY
> Do you have any idea what per cent of the
> Members of the screenwriters Guild earn
> Over $6,000 a year?

Lou waits.

                    O'MELVENY
        Five per cent. That means – 95% make LESS
        Than $6,000. Your old man is starting you
        At 50!

Lou nods. The tailor puts the tape around his neck, measuring.

                    O'MELVENY
        Anyway, it's not like DeMille or Zanuck are
        Waiting on pins and needles for your next
        Script.....is it?

Lou sighs, with a sober nod of agreement. The tailor makes a few notations
down, telling O'Melveny he has what he needs. A new suit will be ready at
6:00 on Saturday. He leaves. O'Melveny pushes the offer closer to Lou's side
of the table.

                    BEACH
        I'll think about it over the weekend.

                    O'MELVENY
        Be sensible. Be smart.

With a very weighted look of advice --

                    O'MELVENY
        And be here Saturday night Command
        Performance. With some good news.
        – (beat)
        Your old man would love.....

                    BEACH
                (reluctantly finishing)
        ...to make the announcement in front
        of everyone.

Hold on Lou's mixed emotions as we go to

INT.   RESTAURANT   SAME

                            17

We're in a very small utility office with Cherie and the manager. Cherie is in waitress uniform.

                    CHERIE
          Look   - I just got dropped by
          my agent an hour ago. You can't do this.
          Not today!
                    MANAGER
          I told you yesterday – you couldn't
          Switch, we needed you. And
          You chose not to show up and hit
          The audition. This has happened too
          Many times. You've been warned.
          You're out. Period.

                    CHERIE
          Just let me work through the weekend.
          Rent's due.

                    MANAGER
          Sorry.

                    CHERIE
          You won't have to pay me. Just tips.
          Please, Joe…!

                    MANAGER
          Good luck with movie land. You're
          gonna need it.

He is called by someone off-screen. He gets up and brushes by Cherie, out. Cherie sits, cursing him under her breath. She tries to collect herself, taking a few deep breaths, while pulling a card out from her purse.

ON CARD - reading: JUNE – FOR ELEGANT ESCORTS – 675-8976.

ON CHERIE contemplating this, her eyes darting to the phone and back to the card. After a moment, she grits her teeth, tears the card up.

EXT.   RESTAURANT   SAME

Cherie comes out, sits down on the curb, takes out a cigarette. She fishes for her matches.

CLOSE ON MATCH BOOK – SWAMIS BAR. Hold as she strikes the match and we go to

INT.   SWAMIS BAR   SAME

SAME CLOSE ANGLE ON SWAMIS MATCHBOOK

PULL BACK to see Lou lighting a cigarette. Casually he leans over the bar's jukebox making a selection.

HE TURNS -- resuming his seat at the bar. As the SONG comes on, Sinatra's "I've Got You Under My Skin", he listens for a second – enjoying the dusty, dark, 'noir' atmosphere. .

A hand falls on his shoulder.

                    VOICE (OS)
              Whatya say there, Lou?

Beach turns: It's BOOTS, the owner.

                    BEACH
                 (nodding)
              Hello, Boots. How ya doing?

                    BOOTS
                 (friendly)
              Just makin' me a living. Haven't
              Seen you for a while – things a little
              Slow in the snoop trade these days?
                    BEACH
              So so. Got a little something – meeting
              Someone. Could be a gig.

19

                          BOOTS
                    (shaking his head)
            Grandfather starts LA's oldest investment
            Firm and you're killing time between
            Nickel and dime gumshoe stints.

                          BEACH
                        (sighs)
            Don't worry, Boots. I'm going
            Uptown – working for my old
            Man pretty quick.

                          BOOTS
            A proper business man! Well – let's
            Have a toast.
He has the barman pour them two shots of whiskey

                          BEACH
            Beer is fine…

                          BOOTS
            Nonsense. Whiskey, man!

Complying, Lou TOASTS with Boots.

                          BOOTS
            Good luck, Lou…..and who knows
            That big story – the one you
            Never found – could still be out
            There…waiting for you.

Lou thanks him as his eyes are now drawn to the ANGLE ON ENTRANCE
where we see Cherie stepping in – framed for an instant in doorway as the
bright, late afternoon sun BACK-LIGHTS her entrance into the dark bar.
ON CHERIE walking down the bar like she's been here before.

                          CHERIE
                      (to barman)
            Tammy here?

                              20

                              BARMAN
            Not yet.

Cherie stops by the jukebox, dropping in a quarter and making a selection.
She turns, heading for the rear of bar.

                              CHERIE
            Mind if I use the phone?

                              BARMAN
            Sure. Want anything?

                              CHERIE
            Bourbon rocks. Double.

Her SONG comes on -- it's the same one Lou selected – by Sinatra!

                              CHERIE
            And don't worry, I'll pay.

ON CHERIE in rear of the bar, over by a small kitchen, removed but close
enough to be heard.
                              CHERIE
                  Jim…hey Cherie…just checking
                  About the class tomorrow, yeah –
                  We're going to do the scene, right…
                  Good, yeah, I'm set – do you think
                  The scout from Fox will show up…?
                  God, please – I need a break, something.
                  You wouldn't believe my day. Tell
                  You later. Lemme know if you hear
                  Anything else about agents – I'm
                  Looking.

CLOSE ON BEACH – listening, and as he listens his eyes take on a soft, bit-
tersweet gleam – gazing nostalgically down the long, mostly deserted bar.
We begin to hear a DIFFERENT SET OF SOUNDS --- barroom sounds of
people drinking, from another time.….

FLASHBACK OF SWAMIS

Maybe five years back and the place is packed. We see BEACH, younger, with
a copy of Variety and he's with a group of young, Hollywood hopefuls like
himself and they're all talking with beers – exchanging news about scripts
and auditions and agents and all the other interests struggling writers and
actors are consumed with.

OUT OF FLASHBACK

As BEACH brings himself around to present. Cherie resumes her seat,
taking a sip of her bourbon. She looks down at Beach, opening her purse to
pay – but finds herself without funds. This is embarrassing.

ON BEACH taking out some bills and laying them on the bar.

                    BEACH
          For mine – and hers.

Cherie smiles.

                    BEACH
          Tough racket. Want some advice?

                    CHERIE
          Not really. But thanks for the drink.

                    BEACH
          Go to Vegas. Better odds.

                    CHERIE
          I hate Vegas.

                    BEACH
          Oz compared to here.

                    CHERIE
          Oh, I hate this town already. But
          That doesn't do much good. Besides,

CHERIE (CONT'D)
it's only those who don't give up,
Who keep going – that eventually
Make it.

BEACH
Yeah. I use to tell myself those
Kind of things. Want to buy a
Smith-Corona? Low mileage.

CHERIE
(smiling)
Yeah…how low?

BEACH
About 250,000 words. Maybe
Twelve scripts.

CHERIE
A writer, huh?

BEACH
(firmly)
EX-writer.
(beat)
Know what per cent of SAG actors make
More than $6,000 a year?

Cherie shakes her head.

BEACH
Five per cent! Which Means 95 per cent
earn less than $6,000! Do you know how
pathetic that is!

Cherie senses his bitterness.

CHERIE
Yeah, for sure – it's a crap shoot.

BEACH
(a derisive snort)
A god-damn fucking bad crap shoot!

CHERIE
So -- what do you hope for?

BEACH
Surfing. Malibu at six feet. Without
A lot of riff-raff.

CHERIE
What's an ex-writer, surfer – doing
In a movie dive like this?

BEACH
(thoughtfully)
Having a last drink, for the last time
In a place I spent way too much time
drinking and thinking like you –
That if I worked hard and hung in
Long enough I'd be one of the lucky
Five per centers.

ANGLE ON FRONT – where a dark-suited individual steps into the bar. He
looks for a second.

MAN (CRAINE)
Is there a Lou Beach here?

BEACH
That's me. Be right out.

The man nods and steps back outside. Lou finishes his drink.

                    CHERIE
        Good bye, then – Mr. EX-writer, Mr.
        EX-hopeful. May your new life be
        Everything your old life wasn't.
        But remember one thing ---
        (playfully singing from "South Pacific")
        "You got to have a dream – if you
        don't have a dream…..how you gonna
        make a dream come true…."

As he's walking down past her for the exit –

                    BEACH
            (smiling)
        Nice lyric. Good musical. But
        Bad reality. I wouldn't want their
        Ending.
            (beat)
        See ya'round.

Cherie watches for a moment as he steps out as we go to

EXT.   SWAMIS   SAME

Lou finds the man waiting by a vintage blue Mercedes, one of those elegant
280SL 3.5's. The door is open and a driver inside.

                    CRAINE
        Lou…?

                    BEACH
        Yes….

                    CRAINE
        Ed Craine. Pleasure to meet
        You. Excuse the rush, but we're
        Running a bit late.

                            BEACH
              Oh, we going somewhere?

                            CRAINE
              Yes. Your client is out at the
              Beach in Santa Monica.

Craine, mid-thirties, short blonde hair, an efficient,   polished manner,
motions for Lou to please enter the Mercedes. Lou looks around a little, siz-
ing things up, hesitates some, but then enters. Doors close and the car pulls
away.

INT.   SWAMIS   SAME

Boots comes up to Cherie.

                            BOOTS
              Where's that roommate of yours?
              It's past five?

                            CHERIE
              Don't know. Supposed to meet
              Her here.

                            BOOTS
                (sighing)
              Let me ask you something, Cherie.
              Any plans for this evening?

                            CHERIE
              Not really.

                            BOOTS
              Got a friend, a producer, in from New
              York and he's asked me to fix him up
              With someone for a big bash he is
              attending tonight.

                              CHERIE
          Who?

                              BOOTS
          Aaron Townes. Pretty big name once.

Cherie isn't convinced. Nor is she unconvinced.

                              BOOTS
                        (lifting an eyebrow)
                    Prime time schmoozing....?

HOLD ON CHERIE still flipping the coin in her mind as we GO TO:

EXT.   PALISADES (SANTA MONICA)   LATE AFT.

We're above the coast highway in the narrow park that runs along the bluff
by the coast. There are two guys right on the edge by the safety wall – looking down toward the homes on the beach. One is a photographer – evidenced by his tripod and camera. The other guy is Neal.

                              NEAL
                        (pointing)
                    It's that one – with the Spanish
                    Tile. Double lot.

The young photographer peers through the camera's viewfinder.
CAMERA POV of the beach house with Spanish design.

                        PHOTOGRAPHER (OS)
                    Got it. Couple guys in suits on guard?

                        NEAL (OS)
                    Right. Now point out to the beach –
                    That's where I think they'll go.

CAMERA PANS from the house out to the strand. The wide beach doesn't
have too many people now – just some kids and sunbathers packing up.

                          NEAL (OS)
                How close can you get out there?

CAMERA ZOOMS in on a pair of kids chasing a ball.

                      PHOTOGRAPHER (OS)
                   Pretty close. Wanna look?

ON NEAL moving in to take a look.

                            NEAL
                     Good. That works.

Neal straightens, checking his watch.

                            NEAL
                  They'll be arriving any minute. In
                  A dark, blue Mercedes. You know
                  What the kid looks like right?

                        PHOTOGRAPHER
                          (nodding)
                  He's twenty-nine. Why'dya keep
                  Calling him a kid?

                            NEAL
                          (ignoring)
                  Get him in the driveway – when he
                  Gets out of the car – and going into
                  The house. Then, hopefully – out on
                  The beach – in discussion. Okay?

The photographer nods – resuming his eye to the viewfinder as we go to

EXT. STREET – EVENING

Cherie in an evening gown – looking considerably more sophisticated – walks down a small flight of steps from her apartment. A chauffer stands waiting by an open door to a dark limo. Her hair color has switched to dark red, again masking her ethnicity

INT. LIMO - EVENING

Where we meet AARON TOWNES, 50-ISH, handsome, urbane, tuxedoed. Cherie sits opposite him.

>   TOWNES
>   Miss Winters, I'm Aaron Townes.
>   I appreciate your being able to
>   join me at such short notice.

>   CHERIE
>   (smiling)
>   My pleasure.

The limo starts driving. Townes pours them each a full flute of champagne. They drink, watching the traffic, the evening sun. At least Cherie is. Townes is staring -- appreciatively -- at Cherie.

>   CHERIE
>   So you're a friend of Boots.

>   TOWNES
>   An acquaintance.

>   CHERIE
>   Same.

Cherie feels Townes' eyes, and looking at him, finds his eyes gazing directly on her. She turns away, blushing. Townes smiles.

>   TOWNES
>   You're very beautiful.

Cherie sips her champagne, smiling.

TOWNES
What part of China are you from?

She doesn't answer right away.

CHERIE
Shanghai.

TOWNES
How long have you been in L.A.?

CHERIE
Eight years.

Townes gives her a shrewd, appraising look.

TOWNES
You seem to have 'assimilated' rather well.

CHERIE
(changing the subject)
What do you do? I mean --

TOWNES
(easily)
I'm a producer. Motion pictures.
Do you like movies, Cherie?

CHERIE
Yes.

TOWNES
Do you go to many?

CHERIE
Yes... actually a lot... I'm...

She looks out the window, nervously wondering if she should tell him about her acting ambitions. She looks back at him. He smiles, quietly reassuring her.

CHERIE
(finishing)
....I'm an actress.

ON TOWNES - his eyes narrow with a certain pleasure, as if he's just been told a wonderful secret. He pours them each more champagne.

TOWNES
Well, now, isn't that interesting.

HOLD ON TOWNE'S AS HE REGARDS CHERIE AND WE GO TO

EXT. PACIFIC COAST HIGHWAY - NIGHT

The vintage blue Mercedes pulls off the highway and enters the driveway of a stately two-story home fronting the beach.

ANGLE INSIDE as Beach glances out the window and several more dark-suited men step briskly up to the arriving car and open doors.

BEACH
(stepping out)
Some welcoming party!

There is a LOUD BLAST OF MOTORS, and turning, the detective sees a motorcade of several more limos pulling out of the large driveway. A pair of policemen lead the departing squadron away. Craine and the driver flash their security cards as Beach gazes anxiously about. He takes a step toward the highway, watching the motorcade streaming south.

BEACH
(to Craine)
You really weren't kidding
about that security stuff.

                              CRAINE
                         (a small smile)
                   Welcome to the big league, pal.

They start toward the house. It is a Spanish design, large and expensive.
Craine knocks, and the front door is quickly opened by a young woman in a
dark maid's uniform.

                              CRAINE
             Hello, Mary, this is Mr. Beach – he's expected.

She lets them in.

INT. HOUSE - NIGHT

Beach and Craine follow the maid through a large, elegant living room. Mary
knocks lightly on the door of a smaller, private den, then takes her leave.

                              CRAINE
                The Attorney General will see you now

                              BEACH
                      You don't mean --?

Craine nods, opening the door as Lou tries to collect himself.

                              CRAINE
                   Go on, man – Mr. Kennedy
                   doesn't like to be kept waiting.

Beach looks in the room. Then at Craine. Then slowly begins to enter as we
go to --

EXT. BEL-AIR BEACH CLUB - NIGHT

Townes and Cherie steps out of their limo amidst the crowded carport -- as
it receives a galaxy of cars, dropping off the flood of important Democrats
for the evening's festivities.

INT. BEL-AIR BEACH CLUB - NIGHT

As the couple continue their way in -- heading for the banquet room where cocktails are being served before dinner. This is a formal setting, with waiters passing trays of champagne, and LIVELY MUSIC playing off somewhere. As they walk through the throng of expensively attired supporters, it is evident by Cherie's reaction there are a number of recognizable celebrities in their midst.

                    CHERIE
                (discreetly)
         Was that --?

Townes nods, smiling enjoying Cherie's reaction. He bends to whisper conspiratorially into Cherie's ear.

                    TOWNES
         Can you keep a secret?

Cherie nods, smiling.

                    TOWNES (CONT'D)
         I don't give a damn, really, about Politics.
         That's not why I'm here. But I do care
         about some of the people here.
         One in particular. Who I hope will finance
         my next picture

                    CHERIE
         A studio head?

                    TOWNES
                (smiling)
         Hardly. Georgie Jordan's --
         hard to describe. He's very rich
         and somewhat opinionated... and...

Townes sees they're approaching a small group centered by a man concluding a story that provokes a ring of laughter.

                    TOWNES
               (frowning)
          Unfortunately -- somewhat drunk.

                    TOWNES
          Georgie!

                    MAN (GEORGIE)
          Aaron!

They greet each other. We meet GEORGIE JORDAN, forty-ish, dark, slicked back hair, dressed with showy extravagance -- a veneer of wealth that tries but cannot hide something dark and vulgar about this short man.

                    GEORGIE
          I thought you were going to be tied
          up all week in New York.

                    TOWNES
          Art you kidding? And miss all this.

He gestures around the room -- it's dazzling swirl of people, the glow of power, the heightened rush, the charged atmosphere.

                    GEORGIE
          It does look to be a good turnout.
               (looking at Cherie)
          And I see you've brought some
          additional support with you.

                    TOWNES
               (introducing)
          Georgie Jordan, I'd like you to meet
          Cherie Winters.

Georgie and Cherie shake hands.

TOWNES
Cherie's an actress.

GEORGIE
(a mock sigh)
I never would have guessed.
(beat)
I'm not familiar with your face,
  Miss Winters. Are you in movies or theatre?

CHERIE
(seems embarrassed)
Well... actually... movies, I guess.

GEORGIE
(a short chuckle)
You guess? You mean you don't know!

CHERIE
Well, I've done a little theatre.
Local stuff. But mostly I want to be in movies.

GEORGIE
(sarcastic)
You and about a million others.
And right now -- let me guess --
you're between pictures, looking for work.

It should be clear Georgie is talking down to Cherie, with obvious disdain.
Cherie doesn't quite know how to take it.

CHERIE
Sure.

GEORGIE
(turning to leave)
Aaron, we'll talk later about your project.
I am interested.

GEORGIE (CONT'D)
(beat)
That'll give Miss Winters a chance... to circulate.

Cherie looks like she wants to respond, but refrains.

GEORGIE
Oh, come now, Miss Winters --
don't look so shocked.
I'm sure the fact a lot of movie people
are here tonight hasn't escaped
even your feeble mind.
I'm sure you didn't come here to discuss politics.

CHERIE
(with an edge)
Contrary to what you might think,
there are other reasons for being here
besides self-promotion.

GEORGIE
(snicker)
Oh really -- you wouldn't want to elaborate?

CHERIE
I'm here, like Aaron because I care about
the Democratic Party. About the future of this country.
And I resent your shallow, narrow-minded implications!

GEORGIE
What implications, Miss Winters?

CHERIE
(angrily)
That just because I'm young and look better
than most of the women here that I don't have a mind.
That I don't know how to think. I
probably know more than most of those same women

CHERIE (CONT'D)
about what's going on in the Democratic Party.
How many of them know what's really important
to the party?

GEORGIE
Which I'm sure you'd love to share with us.

CHERIE
(not missing a beat)
There's nothing more important than what Bobby
Kennedy's trying to do with his racket's committee.
To clean up the unions and restore democracy
to the rank and file of this country.

ON GEORGIE -- staring at Cherie. He could be ready to fling his drink at
her; or just as easily burst out laughing.
CHERIE
Excuse me.

Georgie and Aaron exchange glances -- neither knowing quite how to react.

ON CHERIE - moving to the bar. Ordering a drink. Collecting herself.
Townes comes up behind her.

TOWNES
What do you know about the Democratic Party?

CHERIE
Nothing.

TOWNES
(almost smiling)
I didn't think so.

CHERIE
Aaron -- I'm sorry. I know I shouldn't have spoken
like that.

TOWNES
Don't be. I liked what I saw.

She looks at him, puzzled.

TOWNES
I know good improvising when I see it.
(really studying her)
I guess you are an actress.

She looks at him -- is he serious?

TOWNES
I've got this feeling -- this gut feeling you'd be
perfect for a certain part. It's not the lead or anything.
But it's a fine-featured role. The character is
very important to the plot. And It'll get noticed.

Cherie nods.

TOWNES
You'll have to do a screen test.

CHERIE
Are you serious? What's the picture?

TOWNES
Bobby Kennedy's bestseller: "The Enemy Within."

CHERIE
But I thought you said...

TOWNES
(cutting her)
I'm not into it for the politics.
It's a bestseller. Handled property,
it'll be a huge movie. No promises.
We do the test and see, agreed?

CLOSE ON CHERIE - a lilting elation sweeping her as we go to --

INT. BEACH HOUSE - EVENING

ANGLE ON DOOR opening and Beach emerging from his meeting with Kennedy. Craine is waiting. Beach appears still somewhat stunned.

> CRAINE
> Why don't we go outside?

He motions to an adjoining door leading out to a patio, and beyond that, the beach.

EXT. BEACH - EVENING

Craine and Beach pass through the patio, closing a small iron gate behind them and proceed out onto the sand.

> CRAINE
> What do you think, Mr. Beach?

> BEACH
> I'm a little overwhelmed, to tell you the truth.

> CRAINE
> How did you get along with the Attorney General?

> BEACH
> Okay. Better after he offered me a scotch.
> He said you'd fill me in on the details.

> CRAINE
> Good, that means he liked you. And you've been hired.

> BEACH
> For what -- he didn't really say.

They walk a little further. Beach notices there are some secret service guys inconspicuously but strategically placed along the strand.

> CRAINE
>
> To begin with, the house here belongs
> to Kennedy's sister and her husband Peter Lawford,
> the actor. Whenever either brother is in town
> they stay here. A couple of months back they
> had Marilyn Monroe out as a guest.
> She and Robert became rather close.
>
> BEACH
> (nodding slowly)
> I gather her life isn't in the best of order now --
> and that she's somewhat vulnerable.
> Which is causing him a lot of concern.

They are near the bluff. Waves crash below them.

> CRAINE
>
> Unfortunately, there's more to it than that.
> There's been a rather serious... mistake.
> On Marilyn's part. And there could be
> some very serious consequences.
> (beat)
> Very serious.

Beach waits for Craine to continue.

> CRAINE
>
> I won't go into any great detail.
> That can come later. And from others.
> But the problem is that Miss Monroe was
> photographed without any clothes on the other day --
>
> BEACH
> I heard about that, the Nude Session?

CRAINE
(nods)
It was a prank on her part. Unfortunately, she wasn't as
naked as intended. There was a very prominent piece of
jewelry around her neck.
(beat)
That doesn't belong to her.
(beat)
That belongs to the Attorney General.
His personal St. Christopher.

The words hang there.

CRAINE
Around her neck for all the world to see
if those pictures ever get published!

BEACH
Which, I'm guessing, is exactly what someone wants.

CRAINE
(nodding)
The film was stolen from Marilyn's last night.

BEACH
You said St. Christopher. Is that really so
dangerous? Lots of people wear them.

CRAINE
(shaking his head)
I wish that were the case.
This one was specially made for him as a gift.
It's one of a kind, and quite recognizable.

Craine pulls out a magazine from his coat.

CLOSE ON MAGAZINE COVER - it's LIFE - and it's a summer shoot of
Kennedy at the beach -- in a swimsuit, close to the water -- and around his

neck is a very identifiable St. Christopher.

ON BEACH beginning to understand. They turn, starting back for the house.

>   CRAINE
> There's an election coming up.
> The leadership of the country is up for grabs.
> Those pictures could be extremely damaging.
> Not just to the President and the upcoming election but to the family, their image --

Beach hands Craine back the magazine.

>   CRAINE
> What the Attorney General and
> The President want is for you to discreetly
> try and find the film and keep it from being printed.

Beach smiles, shakes his head -- incredulous.

>   BEACH
>   (hesitant)
> Mr. Craine, I'm having a hard time believing this --
> that the Attorney General is asking me to
> work for him. I'm not sure I'm the man he wants or needs.
> I'm a nobody.

>   CRAINE
> That nobody knows about! And that's precisely the way the
> he wants it. Anonymity. Someone who can do what he
> wants without the whole world knowing about it.

>   BEACH
> Okay, but why not someone already on the payroll?
> You know -- from the CIA or the Secret Services?
> Or you?

CRAINE
(shaking his head)
My primary responsibility is to protect the
Attorney General's sister. Besides, once we bring in a
sector of the security machine, there's no telling where
this might end up. This is a private matter, and he wants
it to remain this way.

Beach nods, pondering all this as they stop near the house. They turn, facing
each other.

CRAINE
You know Hollywood. I've been told you did some writing
at one time. So you're familiar with the business.
How it works, what makes it go.
And that's what we need right now --
someone who knows this town and can find that film.

Beach looks back to the ocean -- He wants it, and he doesn't want it. No
doubt it's the case of a lifetime -- working privately with the Kennedys. But
it also means return to a world he's trying to turn his back on: the movie
world. Marilyn Monroe's world. And he isn't sure he wants that. Nor is he
sure he doesn't want it.

BEACH
So I'm the man.

CRAINE
We hope so. Let me say this --
you're working for Kennedy,
but to anyone else you're being
employed by Miss Monroe.

BEACH
She know this?

43

                    CRAINE
          Yes. But outside of perhaps her secretary,
          no one else will.

                    BEACH
          And you?

                    CRAINE
          I'm your connect to Kennedy.
          You report to me. I'll give you a number
          where I can be reached at all times.

Craine takes an envelope from inside his jacket -- an envelope, which he then
hands to Beach.

                    CRAINE
          Here's your retainer and Miss Monroe's
          address along with some other names and
          numbers that come in handy.
          You'll be expected tomorrow morning at Miss Monroe's.

As Beach takes the envelope - FREEZE-FRAME THE MOMENT WITH
SOUND TO INDICATE A COVERT PICTURE HAS JUST BEEN SNAPPED
OF THE TWO as we go to:

INT. APARTMENT - NIGHT

We're on an antique Buddha, maybe a foot in height -- part of a small altar
setting. There are pictures of family members, fruit, incense burning. Hold
on this, then a woman's legs stepping out of an evening gown. FOLLOW
THE NAKED LEGS as they move to --

VANITY AREA littered with the usual items, but mostly our attention will be
on the assorted collection of pictures of movie actresses -- the famous, glam-
orous ones. There's Rita, Ava, Liz, etc. A dark red wig is placed on a stand
alongside several other wigs.

ON CHERIE moving from the vanity out to her balcony, wearing only a sleek, black slip. She lights a cigarette and gazes dreamily out to the lights of the city sprinkled across the hills. We see her for the first time without a wig, as herself -- Asian. Her hair is dark and long and lustrous, so much more attractive than any of her wigs. She is incredibly beautiful. Hold on her gazing, as we go to --

INT. APARTMENT - NIGHT

We're with Lou in his Hollywood apartment – a spacious, simple, nicely furnished place with a terrific view of the lights dotting the hillside.

ON LOU as he sits at his desk - looking at his Smith-Corona typewriter, smoking a cigarette and having a drink. That's all he's doing – smoking and drinking and staring quite pensively at the typewriter. Hold for a moment, then we go to --

BLACK SCREEN---
AUGUST 4, 1962 -JOHNSON COUNTY TEXAS

EXT. CAMPGROUND - DAY

Early morning in this deserted, rural campground. We see a single man seated at a picnic table. He is EARL, fifty-ish, dressed in jeans and a white shirt, western hat. Earl has seen his share of outdoor work. There is a pick-up parked behind him.

Earl is watching the approach of a sleek, late-model car. The car parks and a young man in a dark suit climbs out and approaches Earl at the picnic table. He carries a sleek, alligator-skinned briefcase. Earl does not rise to greet him.

                    EARL
        You're late. I've got a plane to catch for L.A.

                    GUY
        The extra fifty -- took some time getting it.

45

                              EARL
                    So it's all there -- the two mil?

                              GUY
                       And the extra fifty.

The guy looks pleasantly around the sparse campground.

                              GUY
                     Pretty out here... nice...

                              EARL
                       Yeah... too bad.

ON THE BRIEFCASE

                           GUY (O.S.)
                       Too bad... what?

                          EARLE (OS)
                 It's the last thing you'll ever see.

ON BRIEFCASE -- we hear GUN FIRING (OS). Then A BODY SLUMPING
to ground as we go to:

INT.   BUDDHIST TEMPLE   MORNING

An early morning meditation group. It is composed of twenty or so individ-
uals, dressed in casual, loose-fitting clothes. There are also several young
monks.

A BELL IS RINGING signaling the end of the session.

ANGLE ON LOU, like the others sitting cross-legged, arms folded in lap, eyes
open, breathing slowly in relaxed concentration.

CLOSE ON LOU so we hear a whisper/thought in his mind.

                    WHISPER (OS)
            The wind doesn't move. The flag
            Doesn't move. Only the mind moves.

CAMERA SHIFTS SLIGHTLY – focusing on an elderly individual somewhat
behind Lou. Shaved head, Buddhist robes, also seated in meditation. He is
ROSHI, head monk

                    WHISPER (Beach)
            I don't understand.

                    ROSHI (VO)
            How long have you been working
            On the koan?
                    BEACH (VO)
            Two months.

                    ROSHI (VO)
            Understanding isn't the way. Nor
            Is logic or thinking.

                    BEACH (VO)
            So how do I do?

                    ROSHI (VO)
            Don't mistake the koan is separate
            From your daily life. Your practice
            And life each day must connect

Roshi CLAPS his hands three times.

                    ROSHI (VO)
            Just like that!

SHIFT AND REFOCUS ON LOU still in quiet concentration as we go to

EXT. MARILYN'S HOUSE - DAY

ESTABLISHING SHOT of a modest, Spanish-style house on a quiet street.

ANGLE ON LOU – walking up to the front door. Before knocking, Lou takes a moment to compose himself. He lightly claps his hands three times, takes a deep breath – and knocks on the front door. No one answers but we hear LOUD VOICES of a man and woman arguing from inside. We recognize the woman's voice as MARILYN'S. Lou starts around side of house.

ANGLE ON POOL as Lou goes through a small fence into pool area. ARGUING continuing.

> TOWNES (O.S.)
> Marilyn there is no way in hell he can marry you.

> MARILYN (O.S.)
> He loves me. He told me.

> TOWNES (O.S.)
> But you told me he won't even take your calls.

> MARILYN (O.S.)
> But he still loves me. I know it.

> TOWNES (O.S.)
> I just don't want you getting hurt.

> MARILYN (O.S.)
> You're jealous!

> TOWNES (O.S.)
> Jesus, Marilyn!

> MARILYN (O.S.)
> I feel sick.

A DOOR SLAMS, then a beat, then Townes steps out into the pool area. He takes a couple deep breaths, calming himself. Then he catches sight of Beach.

                    TOWNES
          Who the hell are you?

                    BEACH
          Lou Beach. I'm here on that picture business.

Townes nods, motions Beach on in. They shake.

                    BEACH
          Aren't you... Aaron Townes?

Immediately, Townes disposition changes, feeling the welcome glow of recognition.

                    TOWNES
          Yes...

                    BEACH
          What a pleasure. I'm a huge fan!
          I've loved so many of your films.

                    TOWNES
               (almost glowing now)
          Why... thank you. Beach...
          any relation to Nicholas Beach -- Investments?

                    BEACH
          Grandfather.

                    TOWNES
          Then I'm sure he handled some of my money --
          back in the 40's. When everyone in town was flush.
               (thoughtfully)
          Boy -- have things ever changed!

                    BEACH
          I take it... you and Marilyn...

                              49

                    TOWNES
                  (nodding)
         We're old pals. Been through a lot together.
         Even though I've been away for some time,
         we've always been there for each other. But this--

Townes glances in toward the house.

                    TOWNES (CONT'D)
         This business with Kennedy is not good --
         But thank God we've got a good kid from a
         solid background to help the situation.

He pats Lou on the back as they proceed inside.

INT. MARILYN'S HOUSE - DAY

It is a residence in process, sparsely decorated, things scattered here and there. Townes goes to check on Marilyn for the briefing with Lou. Beach takes a cursory look around at the famous star's home. Townes returns from the bedroom.

                    TOWNES
         She's going to lie down. Just as well. I can fill you in -- Get
         you started.

They sit down in the living room area.

                    TOWNES
         In a nutshell, then: Marilyn received a card
         after the "Nude Session" incident.
         It mentioned Kennedy's St. Christopher being
         around her neck -- and how that might
         appear if the pictures were ever published.
         It was clearly a warm-up.

                    BEACH
         More to come.

TOWNES

Yes. Of course, then, Marilyn remembered
her mistake -- having it on from the night before with
Kennedy. And then forgetting about it.

BEACH

Why was the film with Marilyn and
not in the photographer's possession?

TOWNES

Marilyn had asked for the film after
The incident – saying she wanted to
Think about whether she really
Wanted the pictures published.

BEACH

So the film was at the house for how
Long before the note?

TOWNES

Maybe a week. Marilyn checked it
And found it secure – where she'd
Left it in her dresser.

BEACH

Which was when?

TOWNES

Just two days ago, Wednesday. Then
On Thursday, she decided it was better
Kept with her attorney and that's when
It was gone.

BEACH

So sometime Wednesday it disappeared.

TOWNES

I'd say that's accurate, yes.

BEACH

How many people could have lifted it?

TOWNES

It seems the only person with any sort
of access and some kind of motive
would be Mike Pearl, a friend who does
some astrology for Marilyn.

BEACH

That's all?

TOWNES

Believe it or not, Marilyn lives a rather
quiet life here. In that twenty-four hour period,
there were only the housekeeper and Press Secretary.
And Mike.

BEACH

You mentioned motive?

TOWNES

Struggling to make ends meet, looking
for a break - like everybody else in this town,
someone with a price tag.

The two men nod thoughtfully together. Then Townes writes on a piece of
paper for Lou, pushing it over.

TOWNES

Pearl's apartment. Who, by the way,
has been uncharacteristically unaccountable
since yesterday. I'd bet that's where the trail begins.
There may well be an explanation from Pearl's
end that we haven't factored in.

BEACH

Let's hope. I'll check it out.

TOWNES
Keep me in the loop. I'm staying at the Beverly Hills Hotel.

They say goodbye as we go to:

INT. APARTMENT - DAY

A man is trying to crawl in great haste out of an apartment window, shaving cream still on his face, in undershirt. He has been rudely interrupted by -- Lieutenant-Detective Neal. He collars the man almost out the window and strong-arms him inside.

BRILL
I don't know shit. I swear!

NEAL
Where is he? Where is Pearl?
Don't make me ask again.

Neal grabs the straightedge off the bathroom counter. He brings it close to Brill's face.

NEAL
He's just your fuckin' tennis partner.
He's not your Goddamn brother.

BRILL
All he did was cancel the game today. I swear.

NEAL
(inching the blade in)
No, I swear -- this is your last chance before this
blade gets busy on your face.

Their eyes lock. Brill sees Neal is not backing down.

BRILL
He was trying to sell his car. So it couldn't be traced.

                              NEAL
            Where?

                              BRILL
              Chevy dealer. On Western.

With that Neal, drops him to the ground, as we go to:

EXT. HOLLYWOOD BUNGALOW - DAY

It's one of those traditional courts of small, individual bungalows with palm
trees and cemented quadrangles of grass between each. Beach is knocking on
one.

ANGLE INSIDE

Through a window on Beach continuing to knock. No one is answering. He
jimmies the lock and enters discreetly.

INT. HOLLYWOOD BUNGALOW - DAY

ANOTHER ANGLE as he moves inside. It's very dark, drapes all drawn
tightly. Can't see much. He moves to a window, pulling on the shade tassel.
It leaps LOUDLY UP, tearing upward and flapping erratically. There's a
small-framed picture of a man (Pearl) and an attractive blonde. They appear
on intimate terms.

                         VOICE (O.S.)
                What are you -- lost sailor --
                or did you just wander off the tour?

Beach turns. There's a man in the doorway. Wearing a Hawaiian shirt
unbuttoned. He's got a beer in his hand. He looks like a neighbor. He looks
like he's had a few.

                              BEACH
                        (thinks a quick beat)
              Would you by any chance be Mr. Pearl's neighbor?

                                54

Beach has put a spin on his voice -- making it sound bookish, a little nerdy -
- a whiff of effeminence. Not an L.A. guy.

                          MAN
          Yeah. And we got a good neighbor policy around here.

                          BEACH
                    (holding the style)
          Excellent! I'm so glad. So glad!

                          GUY
          I know most of Pearl's friends. I don't know you.

                          BEACH
          Well, I'm not really a friend. More an acquaintance.
          Mr. Pearl is thinking of subletting his abode to me.

                          GUY
          Abode? Oh, you mean his place here.

                          BEACH
          Precisely. He allowed it would be all right to inspect.

Beach turns, eyeballing the place.

                          BEACH
          He lead me to believe it was somewhat roomier.

He traces a finger along a dusty shelf.

                          GUY
          You got some kind of funny accent.

                          BEACH
                    (proudly)
          Pennsylvanian. Dutch Pennsylvanian.
          Actually, to be more precise -- Halder's County.
          Which is just a little bit outside of Roanoke.

                           55

Beach approaches the neighbor, setting out his hand.

                              BEACH
                    Pheneas McAllister.

They shake. The guy more or less buying Beach's put on.
Which is good. Very believable.

                            NEIGHBOR
                    So Pearl's thinking of subletting... Interesting.

                              BEACH
                    If we can settle on a reasonable rent.

                               GUY
                    Be careful with Pearl.He's three months behind here.
                    So don't get stuck with that.

The neighbor takes the opportunity to hand over a small collection of some
kind of notices.
                          GUY (CONT'D)
                    And you can give him back these --
                    he sold me a car and I'm not getting
                    stuck with his damn collection of unpaid parking tickets.
                    He hands them over to Beach, then leaves.
                    Draining his beer.

                               GUY
                    See ya around, Phibbius.

Alone, glancing around -- something else gets Lou's attention.

CLOSE ON SCREENPLAY

Something about it, makes Lou picks it up. He opens it.

ON SCREENPLAY - Title page: "GO THE OPPOSITE", original screenplay
by LOU BEACH.

ON LOU as his eyes look up from the page, squinting with BEWILDER-
MENT.

ANOTHER ANGLE on TITLE PAGE - where an address is written for a
motel on Santa Monica Blvd. Lou takes the script and leaves as we go to --

EXT. AIRPLANE - DAY
Establishing shot of Dallas-LA flight in progress.

INT. AIRPLANE - DAY

We see Earl sipping a drink in his seat. The alligator-skinned briefcase is next
to him. A stewardess approaches with a fresh drink for Earl.

> STEWARDESS
> Are you sure you wouldn't want me
> to store your briefcase up front --
> give you more room?

> EARL
> We're fine as is, thanks.
> How's the ETA into LA?

> STEWARDESS
> We should be arriving in half an hour.

Earl sips his fresh drink, glancing out the window as we go to --

EXT. SANTA MONICA ARMS - DAY

A dive hotel, four squalid stories of battered brick.

ANGLE ON POLICE CAR - Then INSIDE where we see Neal waiting for
something or someone. He is reading through some travel brochures on Rio
de Janeiro.

ANOTHER ANGLE of the street as Beach pulls up in his T-Bird and parks.
Neal puts down his brochures and carefully watches Beach.

INT.   CAR

With Lou, parking. He scopes out the hotel, getting a read on its grim dissapation. He checks at his script on the passenger seat. Then removes his watch and opens the glove compartment, where he further opens a hidden compartment where he stashes his watch. Then he gets out and approaches the hotel. ANGLE ON NEAL watching the approach.

NEAL
That's right kiddo – room 456.

INT. SANTA MONICA ARMS - DAY

Beach knocks tentatively on room 456. No answer. He tries again. He turns the doorknob to see if the door is unlocked and it is. He walks in.

INT. APARTMENT - DAY

This is a very plain, very small, very comfortless room that has been recently ransacked, not that there's much to throw around. But what little there is has been whacked pretty good.

Beach slowly steps around the mess, taking it all in. The only other room in the joint is the bathroom. He goes to check it out.

ANGLE IN BATHROOM where Beach sees A ZIPPED UP SLEEPING BAG strangely stuffed lying in THE BATHTUB. Beach bends down and starts to unzip the bag.

First we see the FEET which have been hog-tied together. Then as Beach continues to unzip, A WOMAN'S NAKED SHAPELY BODY is revealed. ANGLE ON BEACH obviously shaken but continuing to unzip the bag.

ANGLE ON WOMAN'S upper body and face as Beach is done unzipping. She is young and pretty and very strangled. The rope around her feet extends to her neck in such a way that when she struggled to get free she ended up strangling herself.

The woman's eyes are glazed open in useless fright. As Beach bends to close her eyes, we make she is the girl in picture with Mike Pearl Lou saw earlier.

FRONT ROOM where Beach sits on the bed, lights a cigarette. His fingers are considerably AGITATED and he has some difficulty actually getting the cigarette lit. Taking a deep drag, he glances over the sparse wreckage. He tries taking some deep breaths. Then the light hand clap, three times. For stability. Then he goes to the window, opens it- - and is greeted by a stiff breeze. He looks outside, down below, but sees nothing of note. He turns around.
THERE'S SOMETHING dangling down from the ceiling. We don't know what it is, but the wind seems to have loosened it. Beach gets a chair and steps up.

CLOSER ANGLE so we can see it's brown recorder tape. He gently touches it and discovers he can peel more off. Then more. It keeps coming out of the molding where someone went to considerable trouble concealing it. FOOT-STEPS from outside...

ANGLE ON STAIRS OUTSIDE as Neal makes his way up.

Lou pulls more of the tape out quickly. The STEPS GET CLOSER. He gets as much as he can, tearing the tape off -- securing it into his coat pocket. There's a KNOCK on door.

ANGLE ON NEAL stepping in...

                    NEAL
          Hello, kiddo...

Hold on Neal's quiet, malicious grin as we go to --

CLOSE ANGLE ON PHONE then FOCUS TO B.G. -- where Cherie is kneeling in front of her small little Buddha altar. There is a prayer-like intensity to her gazing at the Buddha.

                    CHERIE
          He said he'd call, he did...
          so he will... oh, please he's got to!

59

DOORBELL RINGS and Cherie's face lights. She moves to open the door. She finds a man there, maybe a little older than her. He is MIKE PEARL a tanned, muscular, beach-boy type. A nice-looking guy who doesn't look so nice now. He appears desperate, agitated.

                              CHERIE
                          (surprised)
                    Mike --

                              PEARL
                    Is Tammy here?

                              CHERIE
                    No.

Pearl steps in, thinking hard, looking around.

                              PEARL
                    Was she here last night?

                              CHERIE
                    I don't think so. Mike, what's wrong?

Pearl lets out a tired, confused sigh.

                              PEARL
                    I don't know. I just need to find her and talk with her.

THE PHONE RINGS. Cherie whirls toward her bedroom, running.

                              CHERIE
                    Wait -- I gotta get this. Be right back.

Cherie races into the bedroom.

ANGLE ON AQUARIUM, as she grabs the phone, resting next to it.

                          CHERIE
            Hello?

It's Aaron Townes, the call she's been waiting for. HOLD ON Cherie watching the fish swimming about through the beautiful aquarium.

                          TOWNES
                     (warm, friendly)
            Cherie... Aaron Townes. How are you?

                          CHERIE
                     (catching her breath)
            Fine ---I wanted to thank you for last night.
            It was lovely.

                          TOWNES
            Yes, it was, wasn't it. And as for today, I've arranged
            the screen test.

                          CHERIE
                     (elated)
            Really -- you mean it?!!

                          TOWNES
            Yes. I've just been speaking with
            Fred Lacey at MGM. Everything's being set up.
            What -- did you think I was kidding last night?

                          CHERIE
            It seemed too good to be true.

                          TOWNES
            Cherie, you've been struggling
            to break in for... how long now?

                          CHERIE
            Seven, eight years.

                              TOWNES
                It should have happened long before.
                I'm only too glad to help out.
                I'll meet you in make-up at 3:30.

Cherie puts down the phone -- STUNNED by her good fortune. She lets out
a SHRIEK OF JOY!

                              CHERIE
                    Mike!! Guess what?!!

She rushes in to share the good news with him. Only he's not there. And
there's no sign of him anywhere. The front door is still open.

                              CHERIE
                Mike --?

He's gone. This feels odd to her. HOLD ON Cherie, puzzled, then --

INT. BEVERLY HILLS HOTEL SUITE - DAY

ANGLE ON TOWNES as he hangs up in his Beverly Hills Hotel suite and
immediately hears a KNOCK on door. He lets in a dark-suited manager.

                              MANAGER
                Mr. Townes -- I believe we have a problem.
                Your check has been declined. Twice.

                              TOWNES
                        (shocked)
                Impossible.

                              MANAGER
                Unfortunately, I will have to insist you
                remove yourself from the premises, immediately.

                              TOWNES
                This is unacceptable. I wish to speak with the director.

MANAGER
He sent me.

TOWNES
Do you know who I am?

MANAGER
Someone without sufficient funds
to pay for his lodgings. You have thirty minutes
or security will be here to see you out.

He turns to leave. Townes thinks hard. Then presses himself between the
manager and door, blocking him.

TOWNES
(restrained)
Look -- I've given this place a ton of
business over the years. Things are a little tight.
Give me a little slack, huh.

The manager looks at his watch, and offers a hollow smile.

TOWNES
(pleading)
Okay -- here it is. For five years
I've been slugging it out in Mexico.
Laying low, real low. Waiting for the right time
and the right project for a comeback.
 But a comeback is only as good as the guy
 coming back. And that's me. Aaron Townes.
I always stayed here. It was practically my second home.
People expect it. It's part of the play.
Nobody's gonna invest money in my project
if they suspect I'm near broke. I'm this close to getting
development money -- I swear. I just need one more day
of "This." Please. I beg you...

And the phone RINGS. Townes jumps for it.

63

TOWNES
Georgie -- Christ -- Thank God... look...

Townes WAVES for the manager not to leave.

TOWNES (CONT'D)
I'm in a pinch. You gotta help me out a little...
Yeah something like that... interim stuff sure...
okay, hold a sec, I'll put him on.

Townes motions for the manager to pick up. HOLD ON Townes, going to window as the manager receives instructions to allow his staying. A huge sigh of relief washes his face -- but one mixed with more than a little concern, as we go to --

EXT. AIRPORT - LAX - DAY

ESTABLISHING SHOT OF THE AIRPORT. Boots' white Cadillac comes to a halt by baggage claim. He climbs out and enters.

INT. BAGGAGE CLAIM - DAY

Boots checks "Arrival" screen. Then walks toward escalator as we go to:

INT. AIRPORT BAR - DAY

Earl is nursing a drink. The alligator-skinned briefcase is close beside him. He sees Boots approach. Over intercom we hear:

ANNOUNCING (V.O.)
Flight 101 to Dallas will be boarding immediately.

The two Texans greet each other perfunctorily. Boots declines a drink. Earl pushes the suitcase to him.

BOOTS
Clean?

                    EARL

       As can be.

                    BOOTS

    How's Bull?

                    EARL

       Who --?

Boots looks at him -- is he crazy. Then remembers.

                    BOOTS

       Oh, yeah. Right. How's everything in Dallas.

                    EARL

       Shit - kickin'! How's it here in L.A.?

                    BOOTS

       Strictly a tour of duty. But my times coming. For all of
       us. Ain't that right, Earl?

                    EARL

       Been a long road. But we're goddamn mighty close.
       Keep the saddle hitched tight.

Boots agrees and walks off with the briefcase as we go to --

EXT. LAX - DAY

ANGLE ON BOOTS downstairs, outside on a pay phone.

                    BOOTS

       I got it. We're officially on. Half-hour.

Boots climbs in the Cadillac as we go to

INT. ROOM 456 - SANTA MONICA ARMS - DAY

The cops and detectives from homicide have descended to do their investigation of the murder premises. Directing things is Detective-Lieutenant Neal, who is digging into Lou. The sense is they've been at it for some time.

> NEAL
> I just don't get it -- how a scion to one of L.A's
> oldest and most prominent families happens
> to be sightseeing his way into a room where a
> good lookin' whore is stuffed in a bag like that.
> I just don't get it!

Lou leans against the wall and offers a shrug.

> NEAL
> This ain't the California Club, kiddo.
> You're way off the map for bluebloods.
> I need something that makes sense.

> BEACH
> Like I said -- I'm a screenwriter.
> I've been doing some research for a script.
> I had an appointment with some guy.

> NEAL
> Which guy. Names please!

> BEACH
> Some guy I met at a bar last night.

> NEAL
> Which bar?

> BEACH
> Swamis. On Wilshire. I got to talking with
> some guy who had some pretty good stuff;
> story stuff --crime stuff. Facts. Details.
> Kinda things you don't get from books.
> So I was going to really interview him today.
> Here. He gave me this as his place.

                              NEAL
              So where's your tape-recorder if you
              were gonna interview him?

                             BEACH
              Said I couldn't do that. First couple times he just
              wanted to talk.

Neal quietly simmers. He knows this is all bullshit, but he can't cut a hole
into Lou's version. We hear WATER SOUNDS from the bathroom as his
team continues.

A man appears in the doorway. Neal turns. Lou -- instead -- GLANCES
DISCREETLY up to the ceiling where the tape barely appears. No one else
seems to have noticed it.

                              NEAL
              Who are you?

                            MANAGER
              I'm the manager --

                              NEAL
              Good. Go in and I.D. her.

Manager goes into bathroom, comes quickly out.

                            MANAGER
              Name's Tressler Tammy. Tressler. Jeez! What the hell
              happened to her!?

                              NEAL
              When she start coming here?

                            MANAGER
              Couple months ago.

                              67

                              NEAL
                    What's the dope on her?

                            MANAGER
                    Don't really know. Paid on time.
                    Didn't really see her too much. Not living here.

                              NEAL
                    Entertaining, then?

                            MANAGER
                    Could be, I guess.

                              NEAL
                         (to Lou)
                    How 'bout you, kiddo? You ever see her before?

ON LOU - A SPLIT-SECOND FLASHBACK TO: The picture of Tressler with
Pearl in Pearl's apartment.

                             BEACH
                         (evenly)
                    No.

                              NEAL
                    Cause in case it ain't obvious, she's no five and dime-er.
                    Not with those looks. Way too expensive for a shack
                    like this. Girl like that is strictly sunny-side of the street.
                    Like you -- Beach.

                             BEACH
                    Me? Because --?

                              NEAL
                         (nods)
                    Because she don't belong here and you
                    don't belong here. That makes two.
                    In my book, two means tango.

                               68

NEAL (CONT'D)
There's you and there's her and that spells connection.
So let's go straight. Tell me what the fuck
you're doing here. I'd sure hate to have this
embarrass your family, kiddo.
But that's exactly what's going down
unless you start with some strait shit.

ANOTHER FLASHBACK: Lou with Kennedy. Lou at Marilyn's.

BEACH
(evenly)
I had an appointment to meet some guy --
to interview him for a script I'm writing.

INSTANT FLASHBACK: Seeing Tressler in picture with Pearl.

BEACH
And I've never seen that girl in there.

NEAL
(simmering)
This could get ugly, kiddo.

Neal's crew brings the dead body of the girl, Tressler, out on a gurney to be
moved downstairs.

BEACH
Lieutenant, I'm inclined to say it already has.

Neal fires a wad of tobacco onto the floor.

NEAL
So how the fuck come you're not "inclined"
to work for your family. Bet that'd be a sweet gig.

                    BEACH

I don't work there because I'm not so interested
in that particular field.

                    NEAL

So how's the script business. Sold any?

                    BEACH

No. Not lately.

                    NEAL

Too bad. Maybe it's time for a new agent.

                    BEACH
              (patiently)
Is all this really necessary?

                    NEAL

You say you're a scriptwriter. That your being here is
premised on being a writer. I am trying to establish if in
fact you are a writer. Writers should have agents. And with
your family you should have a good one.

                    BEACH

That may seem true from your perception,
Lieutenant. But your perception and my life
are two different things -- I assure you.

                    NEAL
              (heated)
I don't need your fucking assurances...
Mr. Big-shot L.A. family. I got a homicide here
that needs some answers. Not some would-be
screenwriter who wants me to believe he's sniffing
out a story. Big family or not -- if you're tied in with
this, if you've lied to me -- I'm finding out.
Believe me, I will. That's my assurance to you.
You just improvised some pretty snappy dialogue

                    70

NEAL (CONT'D)
here, kiddo. So let's call it a draw. For this round.
Address and phone number -- then get the hell outta here.

Lou provides the Lieutenant with these as we go to:

BLACK SCREEN

TYPE IN THE WORDS: "THE STUFF"

EXT. WILTERN THEATER - DAY

Boots Henderson pulls to a stop behind the famed art-deco theatre on Wilshire Boulevard.

ANOTHER ANGLE showing musicians, roadies, etc. moving in musical equipment, setting up for a concert later that evening. Boots gets out of the Caddie, lights a cigarette, surveying the scene -- looking for --

ENRIQUE a handsome Cuban talking over by the back entrance with a girl in the dancer group. He excuses himself and runs up to Boots. They shake hands.

BOOTS
Got it?

Enrique nods and leads them over to a chromed-out Chevy Impala.

BOOTS
What's the show tonight?

ENRIQUE
A great band from Havana.
You spend some time there, right Boots?

BOOTS
Certainly did.

71

Enrique pulls out a newspaper, hands it to Boots.

                    ENRIQUE
          Check out the movie section.

Boots nods, understanding, tucking it under his arm.

                    BOOTS
          Anything I need to know?

                    ENRIQUE
          Huh...?

                    BOOTS
             (quietly)
          Suppositories, right?

                    ENRIQUE
          The best. From Switzerland. Absolutely primo stuff.

                    BOOTS
          How long before blast off?

                    ENRIQUE
          Not sure.

                    BOOTS
          Kind of important. The timing...!

                    ENRIQUE
          People all different. Times can flux depending on size,
          shit like that. Say two to five hours.

                    BOOTS
          That's bookable?

                    ENRIQUE
Yeah, yeah ... Mr. Boots. This is the fucking best.
No one's gonna even guess what hit her. Invisible.
The Swiss are genius in pharmaceuticals.

                    BOOTS
Anyway -- we did our own little test on a
cute little guinea pig.

Boots hands him an envelope.

                    BOOTS
The donation. To the fuck-Castro fund!

                    ENRIQUE
We'll get that prick one of these days.

                    BOOTS
So what's up with these Russians?
Heard there are ships moving in,
unloading weird kinda shit?

                    ENRIQUE
Who the fuck knows with that pig Castro.
Fucking Commies!

There's a call for Enrique to get back to work. The two break up as we go to:

INT. MOVIE SOUNDSTAGE - DAY

We start very close on CHERIE'S FACE as she takes in the activity of the
PRODUCTION CREW setting up to shoot her screen test. Dressed in a
simple but sexy dress, Cherie sits on a tall stool as large lights and a white
cyclorama are positioned behind her. Townes and a young DIRECTOR
conclude a private discussion and the director addresses Cherie.

                    DIRECTOR
Turn, please. Now right.

                        73

CHERIE
Please, can't I wear my wig?
I practiced my character with it.

TOWNES
You don't need to hide yourself, dear.

Cherie nervously fondles the star pendant.

CHERIE
(whispering)
I can do it... I am going to do it...

She looks up, facing the camera, ready.

DIRECTOR
Cherie, tell us a little something about your childhood.
A best memory and a worst.

CHERIE
Going to the movies with my mom.
That was the best.

DIRECTOR
Was this in China?

CHERIE
Yes. Shanghai. We'd go every Saturday afternoon.
My father didn't approve. Thought movies were somewhat
degenerate. But my mother argues she'd worked furiously
hard all week and earned it.

Cherie pauses, thinking, shifting gears -- going in deeper.

CHERIE
We saw just about everything in our little District
by the Bund. The westerns, the MGM musicals,
and my mother's favorites were the classic love stories.

74

CHERIE (CONT'D)
We laughed a lot, my mother and I. And cried --
holding hands.

The director nods to the cameraman to begin moving in.

CHERIE
I think my mother loved the cinema so much
because it reminded her of all the beautiful things
in life she might not get to experience.
We were Buddhists, and my mother was keenly
observant to the many forces of nature.
But she also believed in magic, in the hope of magic.
And of course, I enjoyed going so much because
I worshiped my mom -- and anything she loved,
I loved, too.

ANGLE ON SMALL CREW normally blasé about tests such as this. But strangely becoming absorbed in the delicate poignancy of Cherie's memory. Heads are turned, listening. The set is growing increasingly hushed. Especially Townes.

DIRECTOR
And the worst?

CHERIE
The month of waiting.

DIRECTOR
What was that?

CHERIE
Waiting for my mother's ashes.

The entire set is hushed, riveted.

DIRECTOR
Can you tell us about it?

Like water, like a cloud, like ruffling wind, Cherie's self flows back in time.

> CHERIE
> In 1949, the Communists were approaching Shanghai.
> But my mother's family was in the countryside.
> Needing help. So my mother left us, and went to help.
> But she was routed up with some nationalists and
> executed. My father had already died in the war.
> So it was just my brother and I.

A tear trickles down her cheek. The crew is frozen. Townes hardly breathing, pinching his lip in concentration.

> CHERIE
> So we had to wait for the month for her remains
> in ashes to be returned. There was no money.
> No food. We had to scavenge for everything.
> It wasn't uncommon to see squads routinely
> executing suspected nationalists.
> Death was everywhere. In the air. In the wind.
> A never-ending cry of death.
> And somewhere in all that dying
> was my own mother's cry of death.

She pauses, taking a deep breath, more tears flowing, as she sinks even deeper into another sunken, painful realm.

> CHERIE
> And then the other sound came.

> DIRECTOR
> And what sound was that?

> CHERIE
> The voice of "the never". A voice inside me.
> That cracked me open, splitting me.
> I just called it "the never". This voice that told me
> I'd never get away. I'd never be happy.

CHERIE (CONT'D)
Never have my mother back. Never have love.
Never be able to escape all this.

She's crying now, her pain evidenced and raw.

CHERIE
It slowly bled me, this voice, contaminating
my mind. Stripping me of any confidence.
Leaving me with just this dark, sinister presence.
But at least I had my brother I wasn't alone --
I told the voice. I had someone.
But the voice just laughed at my ignorance.
Saying it can always get worse. And will.

Cherie raises her head, looking directly into the camera with absolute focus,
dead-on.

CHERIE
And the voice was right. It did get worse.
My brother had his own demons and couldn't
take it anymore. He wandered into the countryside
and took his own life. Joining my mother and father.
So I was all alone. There wasn't anybody. Just me.
But even that wasn't right. Because I was gone.
I was dead. I was breathing, but I wasn't alive.
There was nothing inside me. Just this voice,
telling me over and over... Never... never... never...

There's a long pause. Then --

DIRECTOR
Cut!!

The entire set stands hushed, frozen -- stunned. Nobody dares move to break
the spell of what they've just witnessed. Everyone -- from grip to gaffer to
gofer, realizes they've just seen something remarkable.

77

After a moment, the director BARKS ORDERS to break the set down. Townes goes up to Cherie.

                    TOWNES
               (bubbling)
          You know what this means?

Cherie frowns, unsure.

                    TOWNES
          That I should probably be calling Griffith Park.

                    CHERIE
               (confused)
          Why -- is something wrong?

                    TOWNES
          The Observatory -- to tell them a new star
          has been discovered!!

                    CHERIE
               (beaming)
          Was it okay?

                    TOWNES
          We're way past okay. That was brilliant.
          We'll do one more scene, then I'll have a rush put
          on developing it so I can screen it tonight.
          And tomorrow, you and I, young Lady, are
          lunching at the Polo Lounge.

Cherie smiles, and goes off to wardrobe to change, while Townes turns to the young director.

                    DIRECTOR
               (ecstatic)
          Where'd you find her?!

TOWNES
You may not believe this, but I just met her last night.

DIRECTOR
(shaking his head)
This town... you just never know...!

They split while we go to:

INT. DRESSING ROOM - DAY

As Cherie enters and begins disrobing. A phone RINGS. A make-up girl answers then hands it to Cherie.
Cherie takes the phone, listening for several moments before her face crumbles in grief.

CHERIE
(crying)
Oh God...! Tammy...!!

HOLD as she continues to cry/listening as we go to:

INT. BEVERLY HILLS HOTEL - DAY

We're in Towne's suite. He and Lou are grouped near a coffee table, listening to a tape recorder. The feeling is they've been listening to this for quite awhile, trying to decipher its contents. It will be clear it is the tape from the Santa Monica Arms. The voices on tape belong to BOOTS and PEARL.

BOOTS (O.S.)
Don't be foolish. You don't know what you're up against. Just do it --
and the gig and money are yours.

Lou backs the tape up to another part.

PEARL (OS)
She wants me over tonight.

                        BOOTS (O.S.)
              I'll be here waiting until 2:00.
              Oh -- and Mike, don't even think about going
              sideways on me. It won't work!

Lou STOPS the tape here.

                        BEACH
              Pearl goes over. Does Marilyn's chart – the psychic bit.
              She drops off to sleep. Then he fingers the pictures and
              splits.

                        TOWNES
              But does that mean Boots now has it?

                        BEACH
              My hunch is that Pearl went sideways.
              For whatever reason.

                        TOWNES
              I can't imagine Mike mixed up in this business.
              Especially that girl you found. My god --!!

                        BEACH
              People get weird real fast when they're in a jam.
              Or when someone's jamming them.

CLOSE NOW ON TOWNES. SLOW MOTION. FADE OUT SOUND.

We're going internal with Townes. Showing his discomfort now -- about all
this. A discomfort he is hiding rather well.

TOWNES' POV of Lou talking. The tape reel spinning.

REALLY CLOSE ON TOWNES as Lou asks:

                    BEACH
        So who's this guy Georgie they mention.
        Do you know any Georgie.
        Maybe I better let Kennedy hear this tape.
        What do you think...? Who's Georgie...
        what do you think...?

We see a BEAD OF SWEAT about to fall.

                    BEACH
        Should I take the tape to Kennedy...?

Sweat about to fall.

                    BEACH
        Do you know Georgie... Georgie...

BEAD OF SWEAT failing. Hitting the table. It breaks up -- all slow motion.
Then we come out of it to:

ON TOWNES -- looking at Lou.

                    TOWNES
        No. I don't know a Georgie.

And as he answers he reaches for one of the beers between them and "acci-
dentally" spills it – some of it dribbles onto the tape machine.

                    TOWNES
        Oh good Lord! Look what I've done!
        How clumsy of me!

He immediately grabs a towel and begins cleaning up.

                    TOWNES
        Tell me, Lou -- how did you happen to
        discover the girl at the hotel?
        That's not your regular itinerary.

                              BEACH
            I was at Pearl's, looking around.
            There was a script there -- with an address
            on it to the hotel.

                              TOWNES
            Is that so remarkable? Pearl was studying, acting.
            He probably had a bunch of scripts there.

                              BEACH
                        (hesitating)
            This particular script was... well... mine.

                              TOWNES
            Yours? You wrote it, a script?

Lou nods. Townes' prior discomfort is quickly vanishing with
this new revelation.

                              TOWNES
            I didn't know you were a scriptwriter.

                              BEACH
            We just met this morning.

                              TOWNES
            Very true. So tell me about your writing.

                              BEACH
            Sure -- but will the tape be okay?

                              TOWNES
            Not to worry. Leave it with me.
            I'll run it over to Sunset Sound and have
            Post-production clean it up. We might even
            improve the sound quality and hear more. Okay?

Lou nods.

                    TOWNES
         So... the writing. You know I have this Project --
         Kennedy's book -- that needs a writer
         to adapt. Interested?

                    BEACH
              (taken)
         Are you kidding?!!

                    TOWNES
              (pouring them beers)
         Not if the writings good. Bring a script over.

                    BEACH
         I'll bring up the one from Pearl's.

                    TOWNES
         I'll read it tonight.

HOLD ON LOU, thinking about this, this possibility, about having Aaron
Townes read one of his scripts, as we go to:

EXT. MUSSO AND FRANK'S - EVENING

ANGLE INSIDE of this busy Hollywood landmark eatery. Brisk evening
business. Assorted Hollywood types engaged in assorted Hollywood evening
rituals.

ON NEAL nursing a beer at the bar, eyeing "his man" on the pay phone down
the way.

ON KAPLAN 45-ISH, suited but with an untucked, haggard appearance.
The guy is visibly nervous, not in real good emotional control. He returns to
Neal at bar.
                    KAPLAN
         Chief's got a gig downtown tomorrow.
         Then Hollywood Bowl in the evening for a concert.

Neal nods, satisfied.

                    KAPLAN
                (edgy)
        So when do I get my...

                    NEAL
        Hold on. Not so fast.

                    KAPLAN
        Look -- I thought you just needed some
        information on Parker. So I told you the schedule
        tomorrow. So c'mon!

                    NEAL
        You haven't done didley. Kaplan. Yet.
                (to waitress)
        Two more here, please.

                    KAPLAN
        Don't fuck me over, man!

                    NEAL
        You know me better.

                    KAPLAN
        Do I?

                    NEAL
        Sure. Look at all the years I never once said
        shit about your little habit. Always looked the other way.

                    KAPLAN
        So what changed? Why the hooks now?

                    NEAL
        Way it is.

                              KAPLAN
             That's all I get? Two years we rode together,
             doing Fig and that's it?

                               NEAL
                             (sharp)
             No -- what you get is what'll make you survive
             through the weekend, baby. Pure white snow.
             Un-fucking-cut! Put you back on track.
             Send you straight to the Milky Way.

                              KAPLAN
             You wouldn't know shit about good.

                               NEAL
             No. But Larry the scum would.

                              KAPLAN
             You scored from him!

The barman sets two fresh beers down for them.

                               NEAL
             That's right. You help me and you'll
             probably see Monday morning. Life goes on, dig?

                              KAPLAN
             What else I gotta do?

Neal brings out a sheeted, official form, slides it to Kaplan.

                              KAPLAN
             That's a 318. You want me to....

                               NEAL
             Sign it. I'll deliver to Hollywood. In my box AM.

KAPLAN

But that means you'll have to be on call --
Prowl -- Saturday night. Westside. That's shit.
Why would you want that?

NEAL

Way it is.

Neal gives him a pen for signature. Kaplan signs, hand fidgety.

KAPLAN

I'm afraid to ask, but is that it?

NEAL

Almost.

KAPLAN

Shit!!

NEAL

Cafferty. Thomas.

KAPLAN

Coroner's office.

NEAL

Head man, actually.

KAPLAN

Yeah...

NEAL

Need a home address.

KAPLAN

What the fuck is this? Do you know how
tough that's gonna be.

NEAL

And I need it tonight.

                    KAPLAN
          Jesus fucking...!!
                    (beat)
          So do I get it now!!
          Neal pushes an envelope to him.

                     NEAL
          Just so we're eyeball to eyeball.

                    KAPLAN
          What's in there?

                     NEAL
          Pictures you don't want no one in the
          department to ever see. Dig?

                    KAPLAN
          You fucking didn't?

                     NEAL
          Month ago. Parking lot at Tractons.
          Hired a real good guy. B&W's -- caught it all.

Neal has now struck the final nail. He finishes his beer and stands.

                     NEAL
          Back seat of your car. You'll find a little walk
          on waiting for you. The rest when I get that
          home number.

Kaplan shuts his eyes, loathing the arrangement that's just been handed him.
He curses Neal, and tears himself off the seat -- walking briskly out to the
parking lot as we go to --

EXT. APARTMENT BUILDING - DAY

CLOSE ON A FINGER as it goes down the list of names on a directory. It
stops on the name TAMMY TRESSLER/ CHERIE WINTERS.

INT. APARTMENT - DAY

We're on the AQUARIUM, the one we saw earlier, nicely lit -- a striking centerpiece in a normal apartment. We recognize this as Cherie's. The doorbell RINGS. But we stay on the aquarium. The door goes unanswered.

ANOTHER ANGLE side of apartment, as Lou toggles the patio door and gains entrance. He finds it empty.

ANGLE IN KITCHEN as Lou snaps a light on. His eye is drawn to the refrigerator -- where there is a schedule of acting classes for the BUDD BRASS ADVANCED WORKSHOP.

CLOSE ON BEACH as he closely checks the schedule of classes.

                    BEACH
          Oh, shit!

Hold on Lou's frustration as we go to:

EXT. MELROSE - NIGHT

The T-Bird parks across from the unassuming storefront Budd Brass Workshop.

ANGLE ON BEACH gazing for a second at the building, his face creased in a sick, agonized feeling. He takes a deep breath, climbs out of the car and slowly approaches the Actor's workshop.

INT. WORKSHOP - NIGHT

A pair of actors -- Cherie and another -- are fielding comments from class about a scene they've just practiced. Cherie is her natural self, no wig or make-up.

The teacher, BUDD BRASS, 60-ish, is dressed in casual dark clothes with a bright, colorful ascot around his neck.

CHERIE

The character is evolving, shedding her skin.

STUDENT

Seems like she's giving up.

SECOND STUDENT

I agree. Very shallow...

CHERIE

No -- she's finally realized it doesn't matter
what happens to her anymore. Because there is
no more 'her.' Only the situation.

THIRD STUDENT

Cop out, Cherie.

CHERIE

Maybe it's the difference between western --
eastern logic. There's a saying from my homeland --
"the wind doesn't move, the flag doesn't move--"

ON LOU -- reciting the last line with Cherie -- exactly.

LOU   CHERIE
(to himself)
...only the mind moves.   ...only the mind moves.

BRASS

And what the hell is that supposed to mean?

CHERIE
(defensively)
It means... what it means.

                    BRASS
                 (warming up)
        Oh, really. And does that explain your character?

The class LAUGHS appropriately at this, while Brass nods brightly with
them – adjusting his ascot.

                    CHERIE
            It's just hard to explain.

                    BRASS
        I wonder -- does the ocean not move as well.

More LAUGHTER from the class.

                    CHERIE
        I'm just trying to clarify myself.

                    BRASS
        (playing to the class with pomp gravity)
        Oh, yes -- clarification, how very noble of you
        to bestow this sublime clarification for all of us.

The LAUGHTER at Cherie's expense continues. It should be clear Budd
Brass is a master technician at ridiculing his students to the point of tears.

                    CHERIE
        All I meant was the character needed some perspective.

                    BRASS
        Oh -- so the author underwrote the part.
        The character needs additional elements of shading.
        So along with your acting superiority, you also decided
        to benefit us with your burgeoning dramatic
        writing expertise.
                 (beat)
        How many of you writers here tonight
        think the part was underwritten?

No one dares to respond.

> BRASS
>
> Let me tell you something. I don't care if you had a screen
> test at MGM today. That scene just now was a piece of shit.

The students aren't laughing now. They are totally submissive. Rather
uncomfortable for Cherie -- but too scared to front any objection.

> BRASS
>
> After all I've extended to you on the craft of acting,
> you would at least have the decency to respect my opinion.
> And that was a piece of shit scene. I can smell the
> technique -- and that's poison.

Cherie sits, her head beat -- as the public whipping continues.

> BRASS
>
> I could have continued my acting career...

ON LOU - watching this brutalization with a clenched jaw.

> BEACH
> (to himself)
> Bullshit....

> BRASS
>
> ...my agent was sending me parts every week.
> Wilder wanted me for "Sunset Boulevard".
> Ford had a part written in for me. But I chose to teach.
> I chose to share my gift with you -- and that gift is a
> rare, sixth sense -- that tells me, unfailingly...
> (glares at Cherie)
> ...when someone is acting. When someone is false.
> When it's a lie. And I'm bloody never wrong.
> Never! So please -- don't teach me about clarification.

The class, Cherie, all remain in a numbed state until LOUD,
UNINTERRUPTED COUGHING. Eyes turn toward --

Lou is COUGHING uncontrollably. He staggers from the back, racked by spasms of uninterrupted heaving. He slumps to floor.

                         GIRL
          He's choking!

Lou lifts his arm -- struggling for a breath. It's getting serious. Brass moves forward.

                         BRASS
          Does anyone know him?

                         STUDENT
          He's suffocating...!

                         STUDENT
          Food stuck...!

                         BRASS
                   (yells)
          Someone call emergency.

Brass and several others are kneeling, close to Lou. We see Lou's eyes -- pools of screaming white as the coughing continues, and oxygen seeps further away from his lungs.

                         STUDENT
          He's loosing it --!

                         BRASS
                   (true panic)
          No... don't say that... We've got to do something..

Lou's eyes begin reseeding into their upper sockets.

                         STUDENT
          He's dying...

Lou attempts a final focus on Brass, almost prompting the terrified drama coach to move even closer.

> BRASS
> Jesus -- kid don't give up --!

ON LOU as he sees the pure, sweating terror he has instilled in Brass. He lifts his face eye to eye with Brass.

> BEACH
> Gotcha!

There's a stunned moment. Collective confusion.

> BRASS
> What the fuck...?

> BEACH
> Couldn't tell I was acting. Well, well...
> the maestro isn't so infallible after all.

Brass' eyes smoke, realizing he's been duped.

> BEACH
> What was it you claimed: I can smell a phony every
> goddamn time. And I'm not even an actor.
> But I've been wanting to say this for a long time:
> Fuck you! You chiseling little has been!

ON CHERIE - Watching, as a warm, appreciative smile spreads over her.

ON LOU - as the embarrassed Brass PUNCHES Lou, bellowing further:

> BRASS
> Get the fuck out!

Hold on the PUNCH as we go to:

INT. BAR - NIGHT

With Lou and Cherie having a drink in a booth. He rubs his jaw.

                    BEACH
          To be very honest, I'm not really sure where
          that came from. It's actually very unlike me.

                    CHERIE
          You really nailed him.

                    BEACH
          He really nailed me. Five years ago when I was
           taking his workshop. Told me in no uncertain terms
          I didn't have any writing talent. And of course I believed
          him. But tonight I saw him for what he is: just a
          desperately, pompous, self-promoting rake who
          knows how to manipulate and intimidate his students
          into thinking he's something special.

                    CHERIE
          He does.

                    BEACH
          It's so Hollywood, the façade of it. Humiliating people
           like that.

                    CHERIE
          So after he told you to quit -- was that it?

                    BEACH
          Yeah! I was pretty burned out. How long have you --?

                    CHERIE
          Seven years.

                    BEACH
          Full on?

                    CHERIE
              (nods)
          Day and night.

                    BEACH
          How's it going?

                    CHERIE
          As of today...Okay. There's a project.
          I did a screen test this afternoon.

Cherie nods, thinking, studying Lou.

                    CHERIE
          So I guess I can trust you.

                    BEACH
          One artistic soul to another.

                    CHERIE
          How's your jaw?

                    BEACH
              (smiling)
          Wonderful.

She smiles. He really looks at her. In the candlelit booth, she is totally beautiful.

                    BEACH
          Tell me something. The different look -- back in Swamis.

                    CHERIE
          You know -- everyone comes to L.A. to reinvent
          themselves. I guess that's my way.

Lou nods.

                    BEACH
Where are you from?

                    CHERIE
Shanghai. You?

                    BEACH
Here, L.A.

                    CHERIE
Then you haven't had to reinvent yourself?

                    BEACH
                 (joking/serious)
Still trying to pin down my first self.

                    CHERIE
A native -- are you a surfer, too?

                    BEACH
Yeah. Why?

                    CHERIE
Because I'm dying to learn! I was just reading
in Vogue today -- how Mrs. Chandler, L.A. Times --
surfs at --

                    BEACH
Dana Strand.

                    CHERIE
How'd you know?

                    BEACH
We're neighbors. Surf with them all the time.

                    CHERIE
Serious?

                          BEACH
          Sure. It's like Pasadena by the sea.

                          CHERIE
          Your family famous, too?

                          BEACH
                  (pausing)
          A little.

                          CHERIE
          They couldn't help with the writing?

                          BEACH
                  (shakes head)
          They weren't real enthused about helping me
          break into films. What about yours?

                          CHERIE
          Both parents are dead. But they had no idea
          about my dream. Probably just as good.

                          BEACH
                  (gently)
          I'm sorry.

                      BEACH (CONT'D)
                  (beat)
          It's been a rough day for you.

Cherie nods.

                          BEACH
          I wish.... I hope you'll be okay.

She feels his sensitivity, and smiles warmly.

                    CHERIE
            You're shy, aren't you?

                    BEACH
            Some, I guess.

                    CHERIE
            Shy, literary surfer. Good combination.

                    BEACH
            I have a proposal.

                    CHERIE
            Proceed.

They are unconsciously leaning intimately closer to one another.

                    BEACH
            I'm gonna give you surfing lessons,
            and you'll help me with that koan --
            about the wind and the mind.

                    CHERIE
                (smiling)
            You want to know about that?   Really?

                    BEACH
            Yes.
                    CHERIE
                (thoughtfully)
            So... we're back to the finding the first self.

Lou smiles -- really smiles, with a very keen appreciation for the insight
Cherie has just shown him as we go to:

INT. LA MORGUE - NIGHT

We're inside with Neal as coroner-deputy NORIOSHI stand in "The Room"

- a concrete slab with TAMMY TRESSLER lying post-autopsy between them.

                         NORIOSHI
              How the hell did you know?

                            NEAL
              Just a cop hunch.

                         NORIOSHI
              You find a woman submerged in a tub like
              she was and you gotta figure drowning.
              No way would I ever think to check for suppository.

                            NEAL
              So official cause of death?

                         NORIOSHI
              Nembutal OD.

                            NEAL
              What kind of stats?

                         NORIOSHI
                     (from chart)
              Water immersion -- under two hours.
              My guess she was brought in deceased.
              Fair amount of alcohol in her system.
              Nembutal typically takes two to three hours
              to kick in on full. But this way -- bump it up to
              three to four hours.

                            NEAL
              You pretty sure about the time frame?
              About four hours?

                         NORIOSHI
                     (nods)
              I ran several tests, more than required because I

NORIOSHI (CONT'D)
was so curious. I've never seen Nembutal
administered like this. Rather ingenious.
Unless you're familiar with it, it would be
nearly impossible to detect. And you're telling
me, it was just a hunch?

NEAL
(shrugs)
You know -- I read a lot of journals,
that kind of forensic and procedural shit.
I think there was a case over in England last year.
(beat)
Anyway, you'll probably never see
anything like this for years.

NORIOSHI
(pushing slab back into storage)
Then again, this crazy business,
might happen again tomorrow.

NEAL
You said it, not me. Hey -- how
about some Dodger Tickets for tomorrow night?

NORIOSHI
I wish. Got graveyard.

NEAL
Makes two of us. Pair of working stiffs, huh?
No pun. Be seeing you. Thanks for the info.

NORIOSHI
Thanks for the tip.

EXT. THE FORMOSA ON SANTA MONICA BLVD. - NIGHT

Establishing shot.

INT. THE FORMOSA - NIGHT

Lou and Cherie eating, talking -- there is an undeniable chemistry at play here, underscored by their hungry appetites.

                    CHERIE
     Are you going to let me read something of yours?

                    BEACH
     You already asked. Of course.

                    CHERIE
     Isn't this food incredible?

                    BEACH
     Incredible.

                    CHERIE
     Is this all happening too fast?

                    BEACH
     No. It's been forever. Our finding each other.

                    CHERIE
     Right. Can we stay here -- drinking and talking
     and telling each other our lives, our dreams.
     Because I don't want to leave.
     I don't want to go back to that world down there.
     I want to stay here with you.

                    BEACH
     Should I ask the management?

                    CHERIE
            (laughing)
     Yes. By all means. It's such a great place.

101

                          BEACH
        Yes.

                          CHERIE
        Do you know other great places, too?

                          BEACH
        Lots.

                          CHERIE
        Will you take me to all of them?

                          BEACH
        Of course.

                          CHERIE
        But I want to discover new place, too.

                          BEACH
        We will.

She smiles -- looking dreamily out the window at the romantic play of lights.
Lou gently strokes her hand.

                          CHERIE
        Do you believe anything is possible?

                          BEACH
        Deeply.

                          CHERIE
        Tell me. Tell me about believing.

                          BEACH
        There was a book I was given as a present in early
        adolescence. Fourteen or fifteen.
        When I was at boarding school.
        Are you familiar with H. Hesse?

                    CHERIE
          Oh my god -- Demian!?

Lou nods. Cherie closes her eyes. Squeezes his hand tightly.

                    CHERIE
          I know what you're going to say.
          But I want to hear you say it.

                    BEACH
          The book just stole my heart. Had a huge effect on me --
          showed me a new way to look at life. Especially the part
          about falling in true love with a star. That anything in life
          was possible --if you believed with total conviction.
          So something as seemingly impossible as falling in love
          with a star -- could in fact happen.

                    CHERIE
          Exactly. It's partly why I came to LA to become
          an actress.

                    BEACH
          And for me it was turning away from
          the family business and becoming a writer.

                    CHERIE
          Anything is possible.

                    BEACH
          Anything.

                    CHERIE
          Even true love.

                    BEACH
          Maybe the hardest of all.

Without warning she leans over and kisses him. Softly, then deeper.

                    CHERIE
          Promise me --?

                    BEACH
          Promise you what?

                    CHERIE
          That this is real. This moment. Right now.
          What we're feeling.

They kiss again.

                    BEACH
          I promise.

                    CHERIE
          And that nothing like this, has ever happened
          to you before?

                    BEACH
          Never. Because I've been waiting for you.

                    CHERIE
          You're sure.

                    BEACH
          Completely. The moment I saw you in the workshop --

                    CHERIE
          Please -- don't lie. I... couldn't...

                    BEACH
          I swear it. Listen to me -- I'm going to fall in love
          with you. And I'm going to take such good care of you.

                    CHERIE
          Promise me, baby!

                    BEACH
          And you and I are going to conquer this town together!

Another deep, passionate kiss.

                    CHERIE
          I don't want to leave you tonight. I don't want to
          be alone -- in that apartment.

                    BEACH
          You don't have to. We're staying together.

                    CHERIE
          Why is this so easy? So perfect?

                    BEACH
          Because it is.

                    CHERIE
          Let's go home. And put on some Sinatra.

                    BEACH
          Light some candles.

                    CHERIE
          Have some wine.

                    BEACH
          Yeah.

Lou puts some money down and they get up to leave.

                    CHERIE
          This is going to be good.

                              BEACH
                     (putting his arm around her)
                  Very good.

Hold as they walk out.

                              CHERIE
                  So... what kind of Sinatra do you have?

                              BEACH
                  The good stuff.

                              CHERIE
                  The Capital sessions?

                              BEACH
                  Of course

Hold as they exit, arm in arm talking their talk and we go to:

INT. GEORGIE'S - NIGHT

Georgie, Townes, and one of the club girls, NANCY, a sultry brunette, are in
Georgie's private chambers -- a kind of vulgar lair. Georgie in equally vulgar
bathrobe.

                              GEORGIE
                  I had the liberty of drawing up an ad for Variety.

Nancy hands the one-shot to Townes.

The Ad: AARON TOWNES PRODUCTIONS is proud to
                 announce the acquisition of rights to
                 Robert Kennedy's bestseller "The Enemy
                 Within." Principal photography to
                 start June 1, 1963.

Townes nods, impressed.

                    GEORGIE
          Not bad, huh?

Townes continues to stare at it, fixated.

                    GEORGIE
          I also think we should set up a corporate account --
          Aaron Townes Productions.

                    TOWNES
          Georgie, it's a little late to be getting into all of this --
          just now, isn't it?

He checks his watch.

                    GEORGIE
          Now happens to be my favorite time for business.
          You'll deposit this check on Monday.
          I want you to use the Crocker Bank on Wilshire.

                    TOWNES
          Georgie -- please -- I have a bank we can use.

                    GEORGIE
          No. My bank. Fox is into the script for 25K.
          Well buy it out at 40. So there's no haggling.

                    TOWNES
          How would you know that?

                    GEORGIE
                 (hands check to Nancy)
          My people.

Nancy gives the check to Townes. It's for $ 100,000!

                    TOWNES
          This is a bit more.

                         107

GEORGIE

Call it start up. Plus some for you.
Open up some offices. Maybe lease a nice house
for yourself. Point is it's time to move.
Oh and Nancy here is your new gal Friday.

Townes looks at the check. Plus the announcement. There is a certain
uneasiness in his face.

GEORGIE

Also -- there is a contract between us.
I'd appreciate your signature.

He hands it to Aaron.

TOWNES

I'll take a peek and have my lawyer go over it.

GEORGIE
(firmly)
No. I'd like you to sign now.

TOWNES

But I can't. Not without my attorney checking.

GEORGIE

Yes. You will.

TOWNES

I'll bring it around first thing in the morning.

GEORGIE

Aaron -- do you want to make this movie?

Townes is squirming.

GEORGIE

Or would you like to return to that charming
dead-end, coachroached shit-hole life of yours in
Mexico City? What were you producing Aaron --
tortilla commercials?

More squirming, then a sigh. Georgie has him. Nancy hands him a pen. He
signs.

GEORGIE

Excellent. Let's have some champagne.
And don't look so glum, Aaron.
We're going to make a helluva film!

TOWNES
(trying to smile)
Absolutely.

Champagne is poured, passed. They toast, drink.

GEORGIE

That girl the other night, I understand
your considering her for a part.

TOWNES

Yes. Screen tested her today. Brilliant.

GEORGIE
(biting a fingernail)
Cherie Winters...

TOWNES

Yes.

GEORGIE

How would you rate her attitude?

TOWNES

She's a struggling actress for God's sake.

GEORGIE
(biting another nail)
Then she'd sell her mother to the Arabs for a good part?

TOWNES
(smiling at the joke)
Of course.

GEORGIE
Good. Keep her that way. Hungry.

TOWNES
May I inquire about this sudden interest in Miss Winters?

GEORGIE
Let's just say there will likely be a few extracurricular
duties she is in the unique position of executing
that will prove helpful to some friends of mine.

Townes nods thoughtfully.

GEORGIE
And finally... See if you can't get Marilyn to
have Bobby K. over tomorrow sometime.

TOWNES
Tomorrow? At Marilyn's... Why?

Hold on Townes, the question lingering in the air as we go to:

INT. APARTMENT BEDROOM - NIGHT

Lou and Cherie, lying in bed after sex. They are extremely mellow and
comfortable. SINATRA plays in the background.

CHERIE
So you were at Marilyn's today... Jesus.
Did you meet her?

110

BEACH

No... she was in the bedroom. The whole time.

CHERIE

This is all so unbelievably strange...
Tammy... Mike -- those missing pictures,
Marilyn, you with Kennedy... what a story...
(kisses him softly)
Huh?

BEACH

Yeah...

CHERIE

No... I mean - what a 'STORY.'

Lou gets out of bed -- going over to his typewriter – studying his trusty companion, while softly touching a few keys.

BEACH

No -- I get it... believe me, I get it. A story...
maybe a great story.

He moves over to the french windows, opening them for a little breeze to come in – gazing out to the array of city lights.

BEACH

(a kind of anguish)
This city... right when you think it's over,
and you're done with hoping, done with
dreaming -- it comes sneaking back... crawling
Under your skin...

Hold on Lou -- a deep, penetrating gaze at those Hollywood lights. Then - - Cherie comes up behind him, wrapping her arms around him from behind.

CHERIE

I know, baby, it never goes away, that wanting...

                          BEACH
          I really thought I was through with writing,
          that it just wasn't going to happen...
          and Jesus – tomorrow – Night, I'm supposed to....

He can't finish, or doesn't know how.

                          CHERIE
          But this time is different... it's us this time... together.

She rests her head against him, caressing him.

                          BEACH
          Yeah... together... swimming upstream.

                          CHERIE
          Mmmmmmm... I like that -- swimming upstream.
          Maybe we'll even work together.

                          BEACH
          We'll each have a great agent. Working on great projects.

                          CHERIE
          With great directors. Hey -- maybe we'll
          even form our own production company.
          Like Marilyn did.

                          BEACH
          Good. And we'll have a place at the beach,
          maybe even a getaway in New York --
          so you can work in the theater.

                          CHERIE
                   (smiling dreamily)
          Keep going, I love the way this is sounding...

He does, letting the hopes and dreams all spill out -- and REVERSE THE
ANGLE -- going to:

EXT. STREET - NIGHT

POV OF THE APARTMENT from maybe a block or two away. The young photographer from earlier is on surveillance with a high-powered lens - on the apartment.

> PHOTOGRAPHER(O.S.)
> Yeah... the girl's with him. Everything looks cool.
> Right. Check with you tomorrow.

Hold on this SURVEILLANCE ANGLE of Lou and Cherie as we go to:

BLACK SCREEN

Type in: SATURDAY AUGUST 5,1962

EXT. SEASHORE - MORNING

TYPED WORDS: HYANNISPORT

There is PRESIDENT KENNEDY and MALLOY, high-ranking CIA official on the beach, alone. The President is casually dressed, shorts, alligator shirt. Malloy is suited.

> MALLOY
> Somewhere out there, sir -- are Russian Cargo
> freighters churning for Havana. Carrying installation
> materials of a threatening nature.

> PRESIDENT KENNEDY
> Forgive me John -- but right now that's about the last
> thing I need or want to think about. Or can even
> remotely believe.

> MALLOY
> I wouldn't be here, see -- on a Saturday morning
> if I didn't feel it absolutely necessary.

PRESIDENT KENNEDY
What in God's name could the Soviet's possibly be
planning in Cuba? It's our goddamn backyard!

MALLOY
But there's too much data coming in to ignore anymore.
Something's happening down there.

PRESIDENT KENNEDY
So you think Kruschev's turning Cuba into a launch pad?
Right under our noses?

MALLOY
That's putting it a little blunt, but that's the possibility.
Maybe not to launch but for capability.

PRESIDENT KENNEDY
Very, very far-fetched.

MALLOY
Sir -- do you remember what you told me about
Kruschev following your meeting in Berlin?

PRESIDENT KENNEDY
Of course.

MALLOY
You said -- and I believe I'm quoting: you were
overwhelmed by his ruthlessness and barbarity.

President Kennedy nods thoughtfully.

MALLOY
We only need to take a few precautionary steps.

PRESIDENT KENNEDY
Such as?

MALLOY
U-2 Reconnaissance over the island.
We I.D. what they're constructing.
Maybe it's schools, or hospitals. But at least we'll know.

OFF SCREEN A VOICE is calling the President. He turns.

ANGLE ON - A secret service guy.

S.S. GUY
Sir -- telephone. Craine in California.

He nods, excuses himself from the CIA official, and heads for house as we
go to:

INT. LAWFORDS' BEACH HOUSE - MORNING

Craine speaks with President Kennedy from kitchen -- while looking at the
LAWFORD'S BLUE MERCEDES being wiped down by two guys after a
cleaning.
CRAINE
Just an update sir -- as you asked, regarding the
picture business and Miss Monroe. Nothing's turned up.

PRESIDENT KENNEDY
So it's stable?

CRAINE
Not exactly. Tressler was murdered.

PRESIDENT KENNEDY
Oh God --!

CRAINE
And the kid, Beach -- got a little close to the action.

PRESIDENT KENNEDY
Burned?

                        CRAINE
         No. Not really.

                   PRESIDENT KENNEDY
         For God's sake. Jim, keep him out of the crossfire.

ON MERCEDES -- close, very close.

                   PRESIDENT KENNEDY (O.S.)
         Did Peter get a chance to speak with Marilyn?

                        CRAINE (O.S.)
         Yes. She swears the film was truly taken --
         and she had nothing to do with it.

                   PRESIDENT KENNEDY (O.S.)
         I still wonder.

                        CRAINE (O.S.)
         I would not be surprised if the film somehow
         surfaced in a way that will implicate her.

                   PRESIDENT KENNEDY (O.S.)
         Then it's probably a good thing Bobby's
          going over to her house this afternoon to end it.

                        CRAINE
         Excellent, sir.

Throughout this conversation, the camera has been holding on the BLUE
MERCEDES as it's being wiped down. CONTINUE TO HOLD as the call
between the President and Craine concludes and we go to:

EXT. AUTO SHOP - MORNING

We are very close on a near-perfect replica of the blue Mercedes of the
Lawford's. The CAMERA PANS allowing us to match how seemingly iden-
tical the car is to the one we've just seen being cleaned.
But that's the idea: A perfect double.

                        116

ANGLE ON BOOTS inspecting the restored, mint-conditioned Mercedes.

                    BOOTS
               (pleased)
          Mighty nice.

                    SHOP GUY
          Hardest part was matching the blue.
          The guy -- checked it four times. Four different times.

The shop guy opens the door.

                    SHOP GUY
          See -- we even had to put a little nick here.
          Lawford had a few too many after golf at
          Wilshire last December.

Boots nods impressed.

                    SHOP GUY
               (sniffing)
          We even got the smell -- from Mrs. Lawford's
          perfume to match up.
               (beat)
          Plates, odometer -- even Lawford's secret bar.

Shop guy demonstrates a hidden compartment in the glove compartment.

Boots takes out and hands him an envelope.

                    BOOTS
          The final third.

Shop guy takes it, gives Boots the keys.

                    SHOP GUY
          Nice not knowing you.

                              BOOTS
          Likewise.

Boots slides into the impeccably restored Mercedes as we go to:

INT. BEACH APARTMENT - MORNING

Cherie and Lou are having breakfast on terrace of Lou's Apartment Building.
Nothing fancy -- but nice city view. Cherie has been reading Lou's script.

                              CHERIE
          Forget Budd Brass. Forget your parents --
          Forget everybody who said no, or try
          something else. Because you are good.
          This is a great script. I've read a lot.
          I know, and this has something...
          And you are not giving up. Because I won't let you!

                              BEACH
          Honestly?

                              CHERIE
          Do you know how much drivel is out there
          passing off as screenplays?

                              BEACH
          No. I don't get a chance to read a lot of drivel.

                              CHERIE
          Well, I do. And there's plenty of it.

                              BEACH
          Actually, I didn't tell you but --
          I gave a script to someone yesterday.

                              CHERIE
          Someone big?

                         BEACH
        Yeah. A producer. Well... He has to read it first
        and like it before I'll get excited.

                         CHERIE
        He's going to like it. He will. I can tell.

                         BEACH
                      (kissing her)
        Are you always this confident?

                         CHERIE
        Only in love, baby.

                         BEACH
        Then tell me this. What the hell was Tammy
        mixed up in? She's Mike's girlfriend. He's Marilyn's pal --
        one of the few people having access to the

                    BEACH (CONT'D)
        pictures. He disappears. Tammy's dead. And there's that
        funny connection to Boots at Swamis.

                         CHERIE
        Oh, my god. That reminds me. Can I make
        a phone call?

She gets up, and scoots back inside.

                         BEACH
        Use the one in the kitchen...

But she disappears into the bedroom, somewhat out of Lou's hearing.
Lou takes his coffee plates into the kitchen. He pours a fresh cup for Cherie
and takes it into the bedroom.

AT BEDROOM DOOR

CHERIE (O.S.)
Aaron Townes' room please --

Lou stops before entering at the mention of Townes. His face flinches with uncertainty.

CHERIE (O.S.)
Yes -- I'll hold.

Lou backs up, returning to the kitchen. And does not move, trying to figure this out, the reference to Townes. Beside on the kitchen counter is the L.A. Times -- Paper Headlines.

HOFFA TRIAL HEATS UP.
Kennedy indicts on five counts
pension fund Fraud.

Cherie returns after several long moments.

BEACH
Everything okay?

CHERIE
Yeah. Fine. I have a lunch date at the Polo Lounge.

BEACH
Oh... with whom?

CHERIE
Not yet.

BEACH
The "Project?"

Cherie nods. Lou nods back. They stare at each other. Cherie looks at him like "What's wrong?" His face stays blank, unresponsive.

BEACH
How did you meet this "Secret project" person?

                         CHERIE
          I was introduced.

                          BEACH
          By...?

                         CHERIE
          I'd rather not say.

                          BEACH
          Interesting.

We feel a touch of an impasse, a certain chill. They look at each other.
Neither saying anything. Then the PHONE RINGS.

                          BEACH
          My turn.

He picks up the kitchen phone -- looking at her as he does so. Making a
point of taking the call in her presence. It's Jim Craine.

                         CRAINE
          We need to talk. Can you meet me?

                          BEACH
          Where?

                         CRAINE
          Beverly Hills. Mr. Lawford's getting a haircut.
          We'll talk during.

ON CHERIE -- looking at a framed picture of a young boy and a man probably Lou's father. The young five-year-old has a beer in his hand, and the
other steers the boat.

                          BEACH
          When?

                            121

CRAINE

Twenty minutes. Okay?

BEACH

Yeah.

CRAINE

Beverly and Brighton.

Hangs up. Cherie brings the picture to Lou.

CHERIE

Tell me something before you leave and do what you
have to do, and I have my lunch and we won't
see each other for an eternity -- sometime this evening...
is this is you?

BEACH

First beer -- my dad's boat. Letting me steer.
Headed for Catalina.

CHERIE

What a great moment! Does your dad still sail?

BEACH

As much as he can. He's probably on the boat today.

Cherie kisses the picture. Then kisses Lou. The impasse from before seems
to have disappeared.

CHERIE

Thank you for everything last night.
I love your writing. Can we have another
wonderful night later? Please?

He relaxes, smiling broadly, unable to resist her spell as we go to:

EXT. HOLLYWOOD SOUND LAB - MORNING

Establishing shot.

INT. HOLLYWOOD SOUND LAB - MORNING

We're with a PAIR OF YOUNG TECHNICIANS in a production room.

> TECH #1
> Who brought it in?

The other tech guy loops a sound reel and makes some adjustments for PLAY.

> TECH #2
> Some old producer guy, name Townes.

> TECH #1
> So what is it?

> TECH #2
> Listen.

They each put on headphones for the listen. They play it. Their expressions will clearly indicate ASTONISHMENT. After thirty seconds they remove headphones. There is a dark, foreboding look between them.

> TECH #1
> No way!

> TECH #2
> Yeah... but --!

They are both kind of dumbfounded, not wanting to believe what they've just been exposed to.

> TECH #2
> Maybe -- because the guy is a producer --
> it's like some kind of script reading.

                    TECH #1
            You mean actors trying out material?

                    TECH #2
        Right.

                    TECH #1
                 (wants to believe)
            Yeah... right... that could be.

The tape is rewound. Then unspooled, and packaged for customer pick-up.

                    TECH #1
            Let's get it up to dispatch. Guy wanted it pronto.

EXT. BEVERLY HILLS - DAY

We're with Boots as he drives the replica Mercedes along Wilshire. He checks
his watch and makes a turn.

ON CRAINE walking along the street, same area.

ON BOOTS parking the Mercedes. He leaves the keys inside, on the floor
under the seat. He walks away and does not look back. We follow Boots
maybe half a block. Craine is seen on the other side of the street -- walking
toward Boots.

There is a brief nod of acknowledgment to each other. Craine jogs across the
street toward the Mercedes.

Boots turns a corner, smiling -- disappearing.

Craine approaches the replica Mercedes, and slips in. He finds the keys. He
starts the engine, getting a sense of this duplicate version, checking a few
things -- it all seems to be right. Then he starts off.

Boots approaches the Lawford's Mercedes. He finds the keys and starts the engine, driving off as we go to:

EXT. AIRPORT - DAY

The blue Mercedes pulls up to a small helicopter company. There are about six helicopters present.

ANGLE ON BOOTS climbing out of car. He pulls out two suitcases, and walks them into the small offices.

INT. OFFICES - DAY

Boots sets his suitcases down. There's a guy finishing a phone conversation behind the counter. Boots takes out an envelope and counts a stack of money.

                    BOOTS
          Two bags. I won't phone. I'll just show up.
          That's it. But I want the pilot on standby.
          Midnight until eight tomorrow.
          All lights off at night. Tomorrow you're closed.
          Here's the itinerary. We'll be flying south.

The guy checks the itinerary.

                    GUY
          San Diego. Refueling?

                    BOOTS
          Yup.

The guy checks the rest of the itinerary as we go to:

EXT. BEACH'S APARTMENT - DAY

Someone is watching as Lou and Cherie come out of his building and get in his T-Bird, driving off.

125

ANOTHER ANGLE as we see Neal watching from an unmarked car. The sense is he's been waiting for the pair to leave. He approaches the building, entering.

INT. APARTMENT BUILDING - DAY

Neal makes his way into Beach's unit. Neal looks around with mild curiosity, assessing the apartment. Checks a few things. The picture of young Lou with his dad on the boat, gets attention for a few moments.

Then he goes into the bedroom. Opens a dresser drawer. Socks, T-shirt type stuff. From his coat, he removes a small capsule container -- or Aspirin bottle. Inside, we recognize are a handful of the Cuban-purchased suppositories. He removes one capsule and cracks it open. The white Nembutal powder spills out. He wipes up, but allows a trace to remain. The bottle is stashed under the pile of socks and T-shirts, as we go to:

EXT. BEVERLY HILLS STREET - DAY

Craine waves Lou to come into the blue Mercedes.

PHOTOGRAPHER'S POV as Lou climbs in. FREEZE-FRAME HIM as picture is taken.

INT. MERCEDES - DAY

                    CRAINE
          Thanks for coming. The Attorney General called
          me early this morning. He's extremely anxious
          to meet with you again.

                    BEACH
          Why?

                    CRAINE
          I can't say now. But he sounded very urgent.
          I suggest you go out to the Lawford house
          and wait there.

BEACH

All day?

CRAINE

It seems best. The Attorney General's schedule is
pretty choppy. He's flying in from San Francisco.
This Tressler mess has him quite upset.

BEACH

He knew her?

CRAINE
(nods)
She was on his team -- informally called
'The Get Hoffa Squad.' The room there was a
drop-off point. Only it looks like they got her first!
(beat)
Was there anything else of note you may
have picked up from the room?

BEACH

There was a tape, stashed in the ceiling.
I think it was a phone bug.

CRAINE
(quickly)
You found a tape --! Did you listen to it...?

BEACH

A little. It was a sorta rough, scratchy. Probably from...

CRAINE
(cutting in)
How much were you able to make out?

                          BEACH

Not a lot. Boots Henderson and Pearl's
voices for sure. But the bug seems to have
been in his bar -- Swamis.

                          CRAINE

And it's at the lab now?

                          BEACH

Getting cleaned up. Probably be a lot more
to I.D. once it comes back.

Craine nods thoughtfully, pondering this.

                          CRAINE

Listen to me, Lou -- get that tape ASAP and
wait for me and the Attorney General out at the
Lawfords. Very, very important. Okay?

                          BEACH

So the picture business is off for now?

                          CRAINE
                        (nodding)
It's not the priority. If it hasn't surfaced yet,
it may not. Let's put our efforts into securing
that phone tap. Both the Attorney General
and the President are counting on you!

Beach nods earnestly, confirming his efforts to help as we go to:

EXT. BEVERLY HILLS HOTEL - DAY

Establishing shot.

INT. POLO LOUNGE - LUNCH - DAY

CAMERA DOLLIES PAST TABLES of the busy lounge -- and at every table

                          128

we get the turning of heads as if someone extraordinary is walking by. We don't know who, but the effect is clear.

ANOTHER ANGLE as Aaron Townes rises from his table, smiling, to greet Cherie. She slides into the booth beside him.

She looks stunning -- as herself, simple, radiant. It is as if each time we see her now the naturalness of her beauty becomes ever striking. A waiter takes their drink order and leaves.

                    TOWNES
          First -- how are you? That must've been a
          terrible shock, about your roommate.

                    CHERIE
          I'm okay.

Townes looks at her closely, concerned.

                    TOWNES
          Really?

She nods quietly.

                    TOWNES
               (nodding back)
          First: The screen test was excellent.

                    CHERIE
          Was it?

                    TOWNES
          Very impressive. Georgie Jordan loved it.
          Just loved it. Agrees with me completely.
          And he'd like to apologize for his behavior
          the other evening. He's having a little get-together
          this evening, if you're free.

Cherie nods, as the waiter arrives with their drinks.

TOWNES

Secondly: do you know why we're here?
Not for the food. Although we'll have a reasonably
good lunch. There are a few items they do rather well.
No, the real reason -- we are here is for you
to get an agent.

CHERIE

But I have one. Or – had one…

TOWNES

I mean a real one.
    (gesturing to another table)
That table there -- Jimmy Detroit.
From the Morris Agency. Eats here
several times a week -- always orders the Cobb salad.

ANGLE ON GENTLEMAN as a waiter arrives, setting down a Cobb salad.
ON TOWNES AND CHERIE - smiling at the timing.

TOWNES (CONT'D)

The table by the palm. Fred Malloy.
From the Kohner Agency. Swiss.
Impeccable tastes. And even better instincts.
Anyone one of these agents here can pick up
the phone and get any studio and have their clients
up for a picture. That's an agent, and that's
what you need.

Cherie takes a sip, not knowing how to respond.

TOWNES

And unless I've missed my guess my phone
will be ringing this afternoon with inquiries.
About you. Because you're here with me,
they know I'm starting a picture and you are
looking ravishing!

Just then, a waiter arrives, carrying a portable phone. He plugs it in and sets it before Townes. Familiar to this service, Townes nods, then picks it up.

                    TOWNES
          Aaron Townes...

ANGLE OF LOU - using one of the hotel phones just off the lounge.

                    BEACH
          Aaron, it's Lou.

Townes tries to disguise his surprise, glancing nonchalantly around the other tables. He sees one of the other guests also on a table phone and smiles to the individual.

                    TOWNES
          Yes, nice to hear from you...

                    BEACH
          I need that tape. Is it ready? Things are happening --

Townes winks to Cherie -- writing down a note for her -- "Table three, Kohner Agency"

                    TOWNES
          Yes, isn't she stunning?

                    BEACH
          Do you have it?

                    TOWNES
          Not yet. But she is seeking representation.

                    BEACH
              (irritated)
          Aaron... this is real life. Not the movies!
          Tell me which lab!

                    TOWNES
              (reluctantly)
          Sunset Sound...

                    131

ON LOU - hanging up, but watching for a few moments before leaving. Townes continues speaking ON PHONE - for Cherie's benefit.

> TOWNES
> Fred, I'll tell you the truth. Her name's Cherie Winters.
> Yes, she's an actress. Very, very talented.
> She's going to be in my picture, which I think you
> know a little something about. And yes, she does
> have representation however we are always quite
> willing to listen.

He winks at Cherie.

CAMERA GOES IN CLOSE ON CHERIE as Townes is running this down and we see her face surging with an excitement, not realizing Townes' deception -- realizing only that it's all coming true -- the dream -- the dream she's had for so long now -- finally coming true -- hold, then:

EXT. CALIFORNIA CLUB - AFTERNOON

Establishing shot downtown.

INT. PRIVATE ROOM - AFTERNOON

We're with Lou in a room similar to the one we saw him earlier in story with Jack O'Melveny. He has been eating lunch. There is a tape player on the coffee table. There's a KNOCK on the door.

> BEACH
> Come in.

Attorney Jack O'Melveny enters. He sits opposite and looks seriously at Lou.

> O'MELVENY
> Let's see what you've got.

Cued up, Lou PLAYS the tape. It is a phone conversation. Two men's voices. We recognize one is Boots Henderson.

                          VOICE (OS)
                 It's going down. Marilyn is ice.

                          BOOTS (OS)
                 We got a green light?

                          VOICE (OS)
                 Yes. Jimmy's finally had it.
                 The Kennedy punk has pushed him too hard!

                            BOOTS
                 But why Marilyn?

                            VOICE
                 Because they fucked us over. And she's there.
                 Available.

                            BOOTS
                 They're still fucking us over.

                            VOICE
                 So we gotta hit 'em. And it's gotta be a helluva punch!
                 This is bigger than just one deal. It's their whole fucking
                 attitude. It's gotta be dealt with now before those
                 Kennedy picks have a chance to make it even worse for
                 us.

                            BOOTS
                 How we gonna do it? What's my part?

                            VOICE
                 You're gonna rep the Texans. Hold the money.
                 Two mil. Distribute to the inside guys.

                            BOOTS
                 What kind of inside?

                             133

VOICE

LAPD. CIA.

BOOTS

The agency's in?

VOICE

Bay of Pigs fall out. Bottom line there're a lot of guys
with a lot of reasons to hate those Kennedy sons
of bitches. Starting with the old man.

BOOTS

What's the time line?

VOICE

Don't go on vacation in August.

TAPE ENDS. O'Melveny sits in a profound silence, contemplating what
he's heard. He looks at Lou and speaks with measured authority.

O'MELVENY

Lou, listen to me very carefully, I want you to leave
this tape with me. Then respectfully cancel any further
involvement in this matter.

BEACH

But don't you think...

O'MELVENY
(cutting in)
I'll tell you what I think. You are way over your head.
This is something you are not in any way
prepared to deal with. You can bloody
well get yourself killed.

BEACH

That's not going to happen, Jack.

O'MELVENY

You have no idea. I've been around a little more
than you, Lou and I never underestimate
the potential of humans to behave with utter cruelty!
In no uncertain terms, Lou, you will stay here,
make the necessary phone calls and get ready
to attend your grandfather's retirement party this
evening. I'm assuming that's why you're here.

Lou does not answer. And before he can, one of the club's staff discreetly
pops his head in.

STAFF

Mr. O'Melveny -- you have a call on line three.

O'Melveny picks up. Lou waits. But after several moments stands with the
tape.

BEACH
(whispers to O'Melveny)
I'll be right back.

The attorney nods.

ANGLE ON LOU exiting and moving briskly down the hall, He comes to elevator. While waiting -- he gazes back at room he's just left. There's a brief
moment of uncertainty, making up his mind. The elevator opens. He looks
in, then down the hall to O'Melveny's room. But hears:

ROSHI (O.S.)
Only the mind moves.

CLOSE ANGLE ON HAND holding the tape of phone bug – his finger taps
against it – three times.Then, he steps into the elevator, leaving as we go to:

EXT. GEORGIE'S - EVENING

The Lawford's Mercedes comes to a slow stop in the parking lot of Georgie's.
Boots Henderson steps out. He enters the nightclub.

INT. GEORGIE'S - EVENING

Boots strides through the popular main level of the club. Georgie's is a 'swell' place. Lots of beautiful people -- dames, dark-suited guys, muscle guys. There's dancing going on. Highballs and martinis. Boots walks up stairs to the second level.

ANGLE IN GEORGIE'S VULGAR LAIR

                    GEORGIE
          How's the car?

                    BOOTS
          Great. Do we know where the kid is?

                    GEORGIE
          Not too worry. Townsey set it up.
          They should be here shortly.

                    BOOTS
          He really thinks you're going into production?

                    GEORGIE
          He believes what he wants to believe.
          Christ -- He probably spent every last dime
          he had staging this 'comeback.'

                    BOOTS
          Still, he's a great front -- how else to get
          that option to Kennedy's book.

                    GEORGIE
          Good ol' Townsey... he's really no better
          than those two kids. You shoulda seen him
          here last night -- it was priceless.

Hold as they continue on Townes and we go to:

INT. CHERIE'S APARTMENT - EVENING

She steps to the door, opens it -- and finds Lou. She's delighted and gives him a warm hug.

                    CHERIE
        Thank God you're here. I've missed you.

                    BEACH
        We need to talk.

Cherie is quite bubbly and in a lively state -- returning to her bedroom.

                    CHERIE (O.S.)
        I'm listening. Have to get ready. Go ahead.

                    BEACH
        Ready for what?

                    CHERIE (O.S.)
        You know I had a lunch meeting today.
        They're having a little party tonight, the producer
        and his investor. Some guy named Georgie.
        He wants me there.

                    BEACH
                (slowly/concerned)
        Georgie --?

                    CHERIE
        Yeah -- y'wanna come?

                    BEACH
        I don't know if that's a good idea.

                    CHERIE
        I know we were going have dinner and
        stuff, but this is pretty important. I think I'm really
        getting this part.

She pops her head out.

CHERIE
Baby -- I really think this is it.
The break I've been waiting for.

BEACH
(sighing)
I learned some things today. Things not so good....

While she's dressing, and he's telling her -- Lou approaches the aquarium and drops a little of the food there in for the hungry fish. He watches them, still speaking.

BEACH
I really need to speak with Bobby Kennedy
or Craine tonight. There's something going on --
something they need to know.
(beat, as he notices something)
And I'm not sure that this guy Georgie is not mixed
up in it.

His eye has caught sight of something peculiar in the aquarium. He rolls up his sleeve.

ANGLE ON AQUARIUM - There's something SILVERY AND GLINTING in the collection of little 'bottom of the ocean' motifs. Lou reaches in.

CHERIE (O.S.)
But you don't know he is. But Aaron Townes is a fine legit
producer with a track Record and a nomination
for an Academy Award...

Lou fingers out a small, silver canister of film that was hidden inside the aquarium's toy treasure chest.

CHERIE (O.S.)
...The man makes movies, some damn good ones.
He's connected.

Lou looks at the canister closely. It reads: "MM 8/62". He dries it off. Rolls down his sleeve. Puts it into his pocket.

                    BEACH
          And the film he's making is an adaptation
          of Bobby Kennedy's book -- an expose on
          the criminal underbelly of our country.

Cherie appears from the bedroom, dressed in a simple but very effective cocktail dress.

                    CHERIE
                   (shocked)
          How did you know that?

The front doorbell RINGS.

                    BEACH
          Because he wants me to do the adaptation.

There's a long, searching look between them. And the sense of a dark, foreboding momentum at play. The bell RINGS a second time.

                    BEACH
          Who's that?

                    CHERIE
          Townes sent a driver.

                    BEACH
          My... we are going up in the world...!

                    CHERIE
          Please, Lou -- come with me.
          At least you can speak with Townes.

The two look at each other a long beat as we go to:

EXT. SUNSET BOULEVARD - NIGHT

Lou following the Georgie's car, taking Cherie. Cherie looks back through rear window -- making sure Lou is behind.

ANGLE AS THEY ARRIVE AT GEORGIE'S -- entering the parking lot.

Quickly, Lou assesses the situation: there is strategically planted 'muscle' out-skirting the grounds. Lou opens his hidden space behind the glove compartment -- stashing the canister of film and the reel of tape.

EXT. PARKING LOT - NIGHT
As Cherie and Lou move toward entrance. Two dark suited staff stand by the front door.

INT. GOERGIE'S VULGAR LAIR - NIGHT

Georgie and Boots looking down as Lou and Cherie enter.

> GEORGIE
>
> Good girl...

> BOOTS
> Poor son-of-a-bitch!

INT. GEORGIE'S (DOWNSTAIRS) - NIGHT

Cherie and Lou spot Townes at bar, nursing a drink and angle over through the crowd.

> TOWNES
> (to Lou)
> Small world.

> BEACH
> No, small town.

> CHERIE
> Order me a Martini. While I check the little girl's room.

                              BEACH
                         (gives her a kiss)
                      Don't be long.

She trails off toward lady's room. Beach regards Townes for a moment.

                              BEACH
            I guess I have one question. Actually, I have a lot --
            but one right now with an honest answer would help.

                              TOWNES
                      Go.

                              BEACH
            This project -- the book into movie. For real?

                              TOWNES
                         (after a beat)
                      As far as I know.

                              BEACH
                      How far is that?

Townes isn't sure how to answer.

                              BEACH
            As far as someone using someone with a track
            record to get the rights to a book --
            only to keep it from being produced?

Townes continues to think -- facing a harsh possibility he has tried very hard
not to confront. But before he can answer, Lou turns suddenly.

                              BEACH
                      I heard something. Cherie.

TOWNES

No. I didn't hear anything. There's too much
noise anyway.

BEACH
(moving --)
No... It was a short scream... I'm sure.

TOWNES

You're imagining. Here, have a drink. Relax.

Lou turns and looks at him, assessing the extent Townes may be involved
here. Then he turns and moves toward where Cherie seems to have gone. He
stops at lady's restroom and knocks.

BEACH

Cherie...?

Several tries, but after no response he enters.

ANGLE INSIDE Restroom where there is no sign of Cherie. Only a lipstick
on floor. He picks this up. There is a window he looks out --

BEACH'S POV - LOOKING OUTSIDE

There is a rear parking lot where the Lawford's blue Mercedes is parked.
Lou pries open the window -- slanting it out. He hoists himself up and
crawls out.

EXT. GEORGIE'S - NIGHT

Where Lou walks along the rear of the nightclub. As he continues, VOICES
become louder. He moves toward the "GEORGIE'S" sign.

ON BEACH behind the rear of the GEORGIE'S SIGN. Below him is the pool
area.

HIS POV of Georgie, Boots and Cherie. He stoops below the neon sign, hiding so as to hear the conversation below him.

ANGLE ON POOL TERRACE

The three seated beside the turquoise-lit waters, and the magnificent view of the city below.

                    BOOTS
          We want you to 'find' some film. Pretend to that is.
          Say in your dresser. Then report it to Miss Monroe's
          press secretary.

                    GEORGIE
          There will also be a note with the film --
          which we will provide for you.

                    CHERIE
              (confused)
          I don't really get this.

                    BOOTS
          You don't have to. You just have to do it.

                    CHERIE
          But what about Townes' movie?
          I thought that's why you asked me here?

                    GEORGIE
          You can imagine this as a final tryout for your role.
          If you do it convincingly the part in
          Aaron's film is yours.

Cherie is visibly uncomfortable. Georgie hands her an envelope.

ANGLE ON BEACH crouched behind the GEORGIE'S SIGN, watching as Cherie is led away. Then -

143

VOICE (O.S.)

Let's go partner. You're next.

Lou turns and there are a couple of Georgie's security muscle descending upon him. They strong-arm him away from the large sign down to the terrace.

SECURITY MUSCLE #1

(into walkie-talkie)

Okay, we got him. Taking him down.

ANGLE ON Georgie and Boots -- watching as their prey is delivered.

BOOTS

Your concern for her is touching.

BEACH

She going to be alright?

BOOTS

She'll be fine. But how about Lou Beach?

That's what I'm wondering -- will he be all right?

GEORGIE

Let's find out.

BOOTS

It's very simple. Lou. Give us what we want.

BEACH

You've lost me.

Boots nods for the muscle guys to bring Lou closer, right next to him.

BOOTS

Lemme tell you a little story, Lou.

You're a writer, so you'll maybe appreciate this.

(beat)

Back in '48, Texas -- I was working for --

144

BOOTS (CONT'D)
well, just somebody running for Senator.
Didn't really stand a chance.
So me and the others, the group, we had
to get creative. Getting as many votes as we could.
And we didn't always play by the book.
But things, certain things, had to be done.
And someone had to do the doing.
So I came up with an idea --
how to make people cooperate.

Boots keeps his eyes on Lou, but holds out his hand and Georgie brings a book forth, and lays it in Boots' hand.

BOOTS
And that was the book. I'm a man of few words.
I believe a picture can communicate much more
effectively. You bein' a writer might disagree.
But I hope that by showin' you my book,
you'll have a better appreciation for the
question you were just asked.

Boots opens his 'book' for Lou.

ANGLE ON PAGE where we see a half-naked man strung upside down by a long cord of rope. There are two men with blunt bats or pipes in their hands. It is obvious they have beaten the man senseless. Maybe dead.

ON LOU as the next page is shown to him. He closes his eyes, shuddering.

NEXT PAGE - Lou clenches his teeth, gasping. Boots goes eyeball to eyeball with him.

BOOTS
Now you might be thinking that you're
from some kind of privileged family that
you might have some immunity from this harsh
world and its underbelly. But I'm sorry.
You don't. Now -- Once more. Do you have it?

145

ON LOU - a big sigh. Maybe the sigh of his life. He hangs his head and simply turns it.

Boots opens one last page. He makes Lou look. And as he looks upon this last page and sees whatever horrific image of torture he VOMITS.

EXT. POOLSIDE TERRACE - NIGHT

We see a man with a medical case approaching across the terrace.

                              BEACH
                    ...don't know...

Boots straightens up, collects himself.

                              BOOTS
                         (to Georgie)
                    He doesn't have it.

LOU's POV - as the man opens the little leather case and extracts a needle and syringe. He readies it, and with a faint smile, rolls up Lou's sleeve and injects him.

CLOSE ON LOU'S FACE as his eyes slowly close into unconsciousness.

FADE TO BLACK.

SINATRA MUSIC

SLOWLY FADE UP TO:

INT. BEDROOM - NIGHT

A carpet -- stretching towards a bed -- somewhere in the distance. The Sinatra continues.

ANOTHER ANGLE showing Beach lying on the floor.

CLOSE ON EYES as he blinks himself awake, becoming aware of his surroundings. In the distance we hear a SIREN.

Beach gets it together enough to pick himself off the floor. Groggily, he orients himself -- realizing he's in a bedroom -- with its mess of clothes and glasses and a woman lying naked, sprawled on her stomach - one arm dangling off the bed, clutching a white telephone receiver. She is Marilyn Monroe.

SIREN GETTING LOUDER

Beach sits on the edge of the bed, and gently tries to wake the star. No response. He feels for her pulse, then lets her arm fall. She is dead. Clock on the nightstand reads 2:45. He spots an object on the floor near phone -- a plastic cap to the syringe of a hypodermic needle. He sniffs it.

SIREN CLOSING IN
Beach looks frantically around -- he needs to ditch the needle -- and finally hides the syringe cap in the humidifying element on the inside lid of the cigar box resting on top of the dresser. He attempts to leave out the back door leading to the pool area but finds it jammed. He smashes the glass pane and reaches to free it from the outside. Open finally, he gives the room a final glance -- thinking furiously.

He returns to the cigar humidor. Finding a pen, he makes a small inscription on the bottom. Then bolts out of the room.

EXT. POOLSIDE - NIGHT

The siren is really BLARING now as Beach runs past the pool, through the rear gate for the street.

ANGLE ON FRONT as Beach runs across lawn and dives behind some shrubs near his T-Bird as the patrol car arrives.

Three men move quickly from the patrol car to the house. Two are officers, the other appears to be a physician. Once they are inside, Beach crawls over to his car and reaches under the fender to peel off his spare set of keys.

147

Inside the car, Beach checks to see if the film and the tape are still in the hidden compartment behind the dashboard clock. They are. He attempts to start car. It won't turn over. He looks toward house -- the red revolving patrol light hitting his strained face. Tries again. Nothing.

ANGLE ON SECOND PATROL CAR speeding up the street and parking.

ON LOU as he ducks below the window, to hide.

ON LIEUTENANT NEAL as he climbs out of patrol car and inspects. He takes everything in -- the Lawford Mercedes, Lou's T-Bird... He seems satisfied. He begins walking toward the T-Bird.

ON LOU getting as low as he can in the front seat as Neal approaches -- moving for the house. He stops for a moment. Several long seconds tick off. Then he continues inside -- as a VOICE FROM HOUSE calls for him.
Lou tries the ignition again, praying it starts..

                    BEACH
            Come on, baby. Come on!

Finally, it roars to life. Beach whips the car into a wide, SCREECHING U-Turn -- then down the street and away as we go to:

INT. MARILYN'S BEDROOM - NIGHT

As Neal steps in -- checking the scene. There is, of course, no sign of Lou. He tries to hide his angry, frustrated bewilderment from the others. He moves into the bathroom, further looking for sign of Lou, or what may have occurred.

CLOSE ON NEAL as he comes out, back into the bedroom -- and gazes at Marilyn -- her body stretched in lifeless beauty across the bed.

                    NEAL
                (to himself)
            Jesus Fucking Christ...!!!

Hold on Neal as we go to:

EXT. BOULEVARD - NIGHT

Lou parks the T-Bird adjacent to a pay phone booth. He climbs out and goes into booth, dialing quickly.

> BEACH
> (after several rings)
> Craine... Craine is that you? It's Lou.

INTERCUT WITH:

INT. LAWFORD'S STUDY - NIGHT

PHONE ANGLE showing Craine, dressed, in the Lawford's study.

> CRAINE
> Jesus, Beach -- it's 3 AM! What the hell are you doing!?
> BEACH
> Marilyn Monroe's been murdered --
> and I'm being framed!

> CRAINE
> (very controlled, little emotion)
> Where are you?

> BEACH
> The phone sub-station in Santa Monica. They had me.

> CRAINE
> (cutting)
> Listen carefully to me. There's no time to explain.
> Sit tight and I'll be right there. Do not go anywhere.

> BEACH
> Okay... on Cloverfield.

As he's hanging up, A SIREN makes him duck instinctively. Crouched in the small phone booth, he waits while a patrol car screams down the street. It passes him. Lou waits for a few long moments, giving it some distance before rising and heading back into his car.

INT. MARILYN'S LIVING ROOM - NIGHT

Neal is sitting with an older woman,prim, plain-looking, fifty-ish. She is visibly distraught by the chaos enveloping the house.

                    NEAL
          ...so as best you can recall, the glass
          breaking was what woke you .

                    WOMAN
          I remember glancing at the clock on my
          table and it was 2:34.

                    NEAL
          Was there anything unusual before that --
          in the early part of the evening. Visitors or phone calls?

                    WOMAN
          Not really. I'm trying to think now...

As she's thinking the phone RINGS. The woman looks to Neal, unsure who's to answer it now. He nods for her.

                    WOMAN
          Oh yes, Mr. Craine -- he's right here.

She hands the phone to Neal.

INTERCUT WITH:

INT. LAWFORD'S STUDY - NIGHT

                    CRAINE
          What the fuck happened!?

                     NEAL
              (carefully)
          Right now we have no idea. You--?

                    CRAINE
          He called. I'll go get him. Meet us at the pier.

                     NEAL
          Got it. I'll send back up, too!

INT. CHERIE'S APARTMENT - NIGHT

She groggily answers the phone. It's Lou.

INTERCUT WITH:

EXT. PHONE BOOTH - NIGHT

                     BEACH
          I can't talk. But listen carefully.
          I'm in a lot of danger and so are you.
          Marilyn Monroe was murdered tonight.

                    CHERIE
          Lou -- wait -- slow down --!!

                     BEACH
          If last night meant anything, if I mean anything
          to you -- get out of there. Now. Just go.

                    CHERIE
          Please -- Lou, tell me -- what's happened?

                     BEACH
          Go to --

                       151

ON LOU -- he stops, hearing another SIREN... He turns around -- and there's another patrol car heading for him.

INT. POLICE CAR - NIGHT

Two policemen speed down a dark street. Rounding a street CLOVERFIELD -- approaching the phone substation.

EXT. PHONE BOOTH - NIGHT

ON LOU finishing with Cherie.

> BEACH
> The Buddhist Temple. On Normandie.

INT. POLICE CAR - NIGHT

POV - AS LOU BEGINS RUNNING

> POLICEMAN #1
> That's gotta be him.

> DRIVER
> Let's nail the bastard.

They stop, jump out of the car.

> POLICEMAN #1
> Hey -- you -- stop!

ON BEACH running like crazy.

ON THE POLICEMEN giving chase. One of them FIRES.

ON BEACH running past the building toward the rear. There appears to be no access out -- just a high chain-link fence leading to a rear alley.

ON POLICEMEN closing in.

ON BEACH looking desperately around when a car pulls to a SCREECHING halt on the other side of the fence. It's Craine.

                    CRAINE
          Beach! C'mon!

Beach runs up to the fence and scrambles up and over the chain-link. He runs to the car and jumps in. Craine floors it away as the police FIRE after them.

INT. CRAINE'S CAR - NIGHT

                    CRAINE
          Jesus! That was close!

They're both pretty pumped up.

                    BEACH
                (breathing hard)
          Yeah... thanks...!

                    CRAINE
                (concerned)
          You okay?

                    BEACH
                (nodding)
          God... I thought I was a goner.

                    CRAINE
          Don't worry. We'll go straight and
          call the Attorney General.

They drive for a beat.
                    CRAINE
          So tell me -- what happened?

BEACH

These guys, they doped me up and the next
thing I wake up in Monroe's bedroom.
There was a needle on the floor and she's dead
and the cop sirens were wailing...

CRAINE

What guys?

BEACH

Some guys, you wouldn't know them.

Craine bangs his fist against the wheel in anger.

CRAINE

Bastards!

BEACH

Also -- the film -- that was supposedly found
by the roommate, along with a note --

Craine nods.

BEACH

That was a set up, too. She didn't find it.

Lou takes out the canister of FILM -- from the Nude Session -- and shows it
to Craine.

BEACH

I found it! And that tape I told you about -
It'll really bury some people!

CRAINE

Can't wait to tell the Attorney General.

Craine takes it, checks it, then hands it back to Beach.

154

ANGLE OUTSIDE as the car tears down the street.

ANGLE INSIDE

> CRAINE
> Lou -- did you call anyone else --
> about what happened?

> BEACH
> Yeah. The girl, Cherie Winters.

> CRAINE
> She knows?

> BEACH
> (nods)
> Now that this has happened, they may try
> and kill her, too.

Craine nods. Beach glances out the window -- seeing they have entered the POP Amusement Park Pier.

> BEACH
> What're we doing here?

> CRAINE
> I've got some men here I want to start
> working on the transcripts.

EXT. POP AMUSEMENT PARK PIER - NIGHT

They pull to a stop. Craine HONKS twice. After a beat, a police car pulls quietly out of the shadows alongside Craine. Detective Neal climbs out of the car along with another beefy officer.

> BEACH
> (alarmed)
> Craine -- what the hell is this!?

CRAINE

This is the end of the line, Beach.
You're being booked -- for murder.

Neal opens the passenger door and yanks Beach out.
The phone transcripts fall to the ground. Craine retrieves them.

NEAL

I never figured you for this, Beach.

Beach looks at Craine -- an awful realization sinking in.

CRAINE

Like I told you on the phone, officer, check his
prints with those at Miss Monroe's. They'll match.
And don't forget to ask him who he's working for.

BEACH

Jesus, Neal! Can't you see -- it's a set up!

NEAL

Shut up, Beach!
(to other officer)
Cuff him.

The beefy Officer latches on the handcuffs. Craine comes up to Beach --
taking the canister of film away from him.

CRAINE

Thanks.
(beat)
And what was her address again 1490 Orlando.

He offers Beach a gloating smile, then turns moving to his car.

BEACH

Neal -- for God's sake --!

156

                              NEAL
            Thought this was about your career, huh?
            The big break?! You fucked up, dreamer!
                        (to other officer)
            Read him his rights.

The other officer does this as Craine drives off. Beach is shoved into the back
of the patrol car. Neal, and the other officer climb in.

                              NEAL
            Thank God this night is nearly over.

                             BEACH
            Not quite.

Beach rears back and with startling speed, kicks the back of Neal in the head
with his two feet. Neal violently knocks forward into the windshield.
And before the other guy can react, Beach has leaned forward -- circling his
neck with his cuffed hands, and squeezes fiercely. He bashes his head.
Wrestles to get the keys for his handcuffs. Kicks his door open -- and starts
running.

Neal recovers -- radioing for back up.

ON BEACH running into the amusement park.

ON NEAL and the other officer, chasing after Beach.

DISTANT SIRENS crank up.

Beach runs, ducking into a Fun House.

INT. FUN HOUSE - NIGHT

He takes a few precious moments, wrestling with the key to unlock the handcuffs.

EXT. FUN HOUSE - NIGHT

                               157

Neal and partner are getting near the Fun House, their guns drawn. Beach is able to make his way out -- finding himself midway on the pier. Those back-up police are now converging at the Park's entrance.

EXT. PIER - NIGHT

BEACH runs - all the way to the pier's end. He looks over the railing. The dark waves roll in, crashing against the pilings below. He turns, knowing Neal is drawing close. Lou picks out a pop bottle from the trash - aims it at the overhead light, hitting it square -- putting the area into darkness. Then he climbs up onto the rail -- and DIVES into the waves below.

ANGLE BELOW PIER - as Lou SPLASHES into the waves. He begins swimming.

ON NEAL, OTHERS fanning out at the pier's end, baffled to find no sign of Lou. Neal comes over to the pier railing. He looks around. He glances up -- seeing the broken overhead security light. Then he looks below to the crashing seas.

> NEAL
> (bitter, but with a nod of respect)
> Goddamn son-of-a-bitch...!!

Hold on Neal as he looks below and we go to:

EXT. MARILYN'S HOME - NEAR DAWN

Establishing shot - showing more police cars, an ambulance, and an overall heightened level of activity. A few early reporters are trying unsuccessfully to gain entrance inside. A smattering of fans.

INT. THE BEDROOM - NEAR DAWN

Police and investigators attempting to do their work of clue gathering and procedural diligence despite the repeated interruptions from persons attached to Marilyn's career. The press secretary. Her psychiatrist. A voice yells DIMAGGIO insists on speaking with someone immediately.

PETER LAWFORD watches glumly while Marilyn is transferred from the bed into a gurney bag, readied for the ambulance and the trip to the morgue. An OFFICER is trying to end a conversation with him.

> OFFICER
> We have a reliable witness --
> someone was seen running out of here, for the street.

> LAWFORD
> Impossible. Marilyn was by herself all evening.
> I swear it. She called me. It's absolutely true.

The officer moves with the gurney attendants from the bedroom into the main section of the home. Lawford follows. Conversation continues.

> OFFICER
> Mr. Lawford, with all due respect -- you are the
> President's brother-in-law, but we're trying
> to conduct a possible homicide.
> And you're really not allowed in here.

> LAWFORD
> Homicide!! You can't mean it!
> What possible indication --?!

ANGLE AS THEY ROUTE with the gurney outside.

EXT. MARILYN'S HOUSE - NIGHT

> OFFICER
> The broken window in the bedroom for starters.

> LAWFORD
> (insistent)
> No... no... I was here earlier in the afternoon.
> Marilyn showed me. It was her accident. It's true!

The gurney is wheeled up to the ambulance. CAMERA FLASHES go off.

OFFICER

Not according to the housekeeper.
We'll get your official statement later. Now please.

LAWFORD

At least tell me who this eyewitness is --
who saw this 'someone' running off?

ON THE BACK OF THE AMBULANCE as the body bag with Marilyn is moved from the gurney and slid inside. The doors are slammed shut.

OFFICER

One of the first officers to arrive. Lieutenant Neal.

Hold on Lawford as he watches as the ambulance starts up and moves out, taking Marilyn to the morgue.

OFFICER

Oh, and Mr. Lawford... your car, the blue Mercedes is here.

LAWFORD

Impossible. It's at the house. I drove the Alpha.

The officer patiently directs Lawford's attention to the blue Mercedes. Lawford obviously missed it in the fray when entering. As it is, his eyes widen and his jaw visibly drops in astonishment. Until a seeping realization darkens his face.

FOLLOW LAWFORD

INT. MARILYN'S LIVING ROOM - NIGHT

-- into the house, where he finds a phone, and dials a number.

LAWFORD

Bobby -- Peter. At Marilyn's. This is a bloody nightmare! Collateral doesn't begin to describe it! You've got to get Parker involved immediately. I'll do what I can here, but it might be too late.

160

EXT. BEACH - DAWN

The rear of a Surf Woody is opened and two surfer guys pull out their boards for an early morning go-out. They hide their keys under rear fender, and head out to the waves.

ANGLE ON LOU watching from a vantage point down the beach.

ON BEACH approaching car as the surfers paddle out. He finds the key, opens the car and drives off.

EXT. BUDDHIST CENTER - MORNING

This is a house in a residential neighborhood that has been converted into a Buddhist retreat and center. Nice grounds. Quiet, contemplative - serene. Lou approaches up the gravel walkway toward front -- where Cherie is seated by front entrance -- a beautiful antique red door. In the B.G. we hear THE MONKS CHANTING.

Cherie rushes into his arms. And they kiss.

                    CHERIE
          Wow! You're okay?!

                    BEACH
          Barely. Why didn't you go inside?

                    CHERIE
          They were chanting. I didn't want to disturb.

                    BEACH
          Let's go in -- have I got a lot to tell.

                    CHERIE
          Lou -- I can't stay long, I'm going to Palm Springs.

Lou looks at her, squinting.

                    BEACH
No... you're not!

                    CHERIE
But -- Townes is picking me up.
We're going out to the desert, Palm Springs
to meet the director. He's on location.

Beach lets out a long, exasperated SIGH. He opens the door and they step
inside.

                    BEACH
There's a war going on. Between Bobby Kennedy
and Hoffa. And three people have died in that
war -- Tammy, Mike, and now Marilyn.

                    CHERIE
Yeah -- okay -- fine. I'm sorry and it's terrible.
But that doesn't mean the world stops.
That I give up.

                    BEACH
        (angry)
Will you stop with this fucking movie business!

                    CHERIE
No! I won't!

                    BEACH
You're not hearing me. People have killed Marilyn.
And they know you know. Which means you
know too much. Which means Townes isn't coming
over. Someone else will. To make sure you'll never talk.

                    CHERIE
Aaron's not part of it. I can trust him.

                         BEACH
        Not anymore. Things are too deep.
        You can't trust anyone.

Cherie looks at him a long beat.

                         CHERIE
        Maybe that goes for you, too.

They look at each other a long beat.

                         CHERIE
        I mean who the fuck are you anyway.
        We spent one night together.

                         BEACH
        That's a cheap shot!

                         CHERIE
        Yeah. And I know a little something about
        cheap shots. I've had seven years on the frontlines
        of cheap shots in this town.

                         BEACH
        Yeah -- you're a real pro at that --
        struggling... struggling so hard you played
        right along with Georgie. Like any good pro would do.

She glowers at him. Then SLAPS him.

After a beat, he SLAPS her back.

                         CHERIE
                    (near tears)
        You think I wanted to? It was either that or --

                         BEACH
        -- or no part.

                          163

                    CHERIE

          Lou -- you know how hard it is getting started
          in this town. You went through it.
          You know that hunger -- how it eats your heart out --
          waiting and struggling year after year.

Beach eases, looking at her gently, understanding.

                    BEACH
                (with care)
          You may not want to hear this --
          but I'm going to tell it: they're using you. And that's all.

She's really near tears now -- because she knows in her heart what he's saying is true. And that hurts. Beach puts his arm around her, kissing her.

                    BEACH
          They used you and they used me.
          We were both sucked into it. Even Townes --
          They were using him to get the rights
          to Kennedy's book. Not to make it -- but to insure it
          wouldn't get produced.

                    CHERIE
                (crying)
          But... I was so close.

                    BEACH
          I know, Angel. It's tough when you're that close.

                    CHERIE
          I wanted so bad to believe it. That this time it was finally
          going to happen.

                    BEACH
          Yeah -- me, too... that's our curse, we
          can't stop it, the damn dreaming.

Roshi comes padding down the hallway toward Lou and Cherie.

                    BEACH
          Sorry, Roshi -- but I'm in a bit of a mess.
          Can we stay for awhile?

Roshi nods, of course, and closes the door after them.

                    ROSHI
          Are you in danger?

                    BEACH
               (nods)
          Some very bad men would like to find me
          and end my life.

                    ROSHI
          Then better stay here.

                    BEACH
          Oh yes! I am not budging. This is the only safe place
          left us. We sit tight and wait for the cavalry.

                    ROSHI
          Cavalry?

                    BEACH
          The men who will come and safe us.
          May I use the phone to call them?

Roshi nods, and leads them into the quarters as we go to

INT. HOTEL SUITE - MORNING

In San Francisco, of BOBBY KENNEDY, on the phone - in a crisis-like discussion. An AIDE signals another line is waiting for him, a Lou Beach from L.A.

KENNEDY

Okay... find out who's in charge of the autopsy
and have Parker call me back.

He hangs up and takes the other phone line -- to Lou.

KENNEDY

Lou -- for God's sake -- tell me what happened.

ANGLE ON TV SET in the corner of the suite that is turned to coverage of
Marilyn's death. We will stay on this for the duration of the conversation.
There is a newscaster out front of the actress' Brentwood home -- giving us
an ON-SITE feel for the fans who have gathered in mourning.

Very shortly, the newscast will spin into a brief bio of Marilyn -- her career
with accompanying clips from her memorable films. Conversations are all
OFF-SCREEN between Kennedy and Beach.

BEACH (O.S.)

Marilyn was murdered. Hoffa, I'm pretty sure,
engineered it. And your sister's bodyguard,
Craine, was the inside guy.

KENNEDY (O.S.)

Craine -- you know this for a fact?

BEACH (O.S.)

Yes. He double-crossed me. I called him for help --
but he took me to the cops -- to hand me in.
See, they doped me, then dropped me in
Marilyn's bedroom to make it look like I killed her.
And then they tipped the cops.
I scraped off just before they were able to snatch me.

KENNEDY (O.S.)

But why would they make you the fall guy?

BEACH (O.S.)

To make it look like you had her killed.
 They catch me -- then connect me to you --
and it's all over.

KENNEDY (O.S.)
Jesus -- I can't believe that about Craine!

ON THE TV we see Marilyn in Korea entertaining the troops.

KENNEDY (O.S.)
Jim was the one who suggested hiring a
detective to find the film.

BEACH (O.S.)
Thai's another thing -- Marilyn didn't put
Pearl up to it. She had nothing to do with it.
They had the girl pretend to find it with
the note so it would make Marilyn look bad --
even dangerous -- to you.

KENNEDY (O.S.)
There's the motive for the murder theory.

BEACH (O.S.)
Exactly! To hush her up from embarrassing
you and your family.

KENNEDY (O.S.)
Jesus! That bastard.
(beat)
So where's the film now -- I'm presuming by
what you're saying it wasn't destroyed.

BEACH (O.S.)
No, I had it -- but Craine tricked it away from me.

KENNEDY (O.S.)
So it could still be developed and published?

BEACH (O.S.)
Unfortunately.

Silence. There's MARILYN on the screen in the famous skirt shot from the Seven Year Itch.

                    KENNEDY (O.S.)
          Where are you now?

                    BEACH (O.S.)
          Basically on the lam.

                    KENNEDY (O.S.)
          Lou -- I'll be talking with the L.A. Police immediately
          and try to stabilize this terrible situation.
          But if those pictures get into print and the
          media takes over -- I'm not certain how
          far I'll be able to control this.

                    BEACH (O.S.)
          Yeah...

                    KENNEDY (O.S.)
          Is there anyway -- any possible way you
          can get that film back from Craine?

                    BEACH (O.S.)
          Jeez -- I don't know... I barely scraped out of
          two impossible jams. It's kind of lucky I'm
          even talking with you now.

                    KENNEDY (O.S.)
          Lou -- I understand what you're probably
          up against, what I'm asking -- but please.
          If you could...! If there's any possible way --!

ON LOU - as a SWAMIS MATCHBOOK is placed in his hand, He looks up -- seeing Roshi.

                    BEACH
          I'll do what I can.

BEACH (CONT'D)
(beat)
Call Aaron Townes. At the Beverly Hills Hotel.
Have him meet me at Swamis, it's a bar on Wilshire.
In thirty minutes. With a gun, if possible.

ANGLE ON LOU as he hangs up with the Attorney General, back in the Zen
Center. Lou checks the matchbook, then Roshi

ROSHI
Keep lit.

BEACH
Keep what lit?

ROSHI
(with compassion)
The Dharma. Always. Most important.
Then, no matter what, never any problem.
Everything okay. Big or small. Doesn't matter.

Lou nods, looking at the matches, then at Roshi.

BEACH
The Koan...

ROSHI
Your koan.

BEACH
(nodding)
No city for dreaming.

ROSHI
(big smile)
Good answer.

Hold on their look as we go to:

169

EXT. SWAMIS - MORNING

The place is dark and grim and shady without the familiar sign on. Boot's unmistakable Cadillac is on the side.

ANGLE IN WOODY as Beach switches off the motor and turns to Cherie.

> BEACH
> No matter what happens in there, we're not going to be able to just walk away from this. We both know too much.

> CHERIE
> Won't the Kennedys help?

> BEACH
> Yes -- but --
> (shrugs)
> -- who knows. Maybe we should go down to Mexico for awhile. Until things cool down. Then arrange something.

> CHERIE
> (sighing)
> Why did all this have to happen...?
> Why couldn't we have met -- like normal people meet?

He moves for her, tenderly taking her in his arms.

> BEACH
> And gone out to dinner?

> CHERIE
> (smiling)
> Seen a movie... walked along the beach.
> Hey -- don't forget -- those surfing lessons.

                              BEACH
                      (brushing a loose hair back)
                  We will. We'll do all that. And more.

ANGLE ON TOWNES pulling up, parking behind Beach.

ANGLE ON Beach and Cherie. They look at each other a long beat.
Then embrace tightly and kiss.

                             CHERIE
                          (whispering)
                    What's it like for you?

                              BEACH
                  Hoping we're together like this on a
                  train for Mexico tonight.

                             CHERIE
                    Then here's to Mexico.

They kiss goodbye. Beach climbs out, and runs back to Townes' car.

                              BEACH
                  Give me fifteen minutes in there.
                  If I'm not out by then, step into the bar.

                             TOWNES
             Okay, and I want first option for the story.

                              BEACH
                          (a tight smile)
                  Let's just get through it.

Beach crosses the street and enters Swamis.

INT. SWAMIS - NIGHT

                               171

It's empty except for the barman, behind the bar setting up for the day. The existing bleak lighting gives it a coarse, dusty edge.

> BEACH
>
> Can a guy get an eye opener?

The barman stiffens at his unexpected presence.

> BARMAN
>
> Not opened yet.

> BEACH
>
> Thought I saw some cars out front.

> BARMAN
>
> Ain't nobody here, shamus.

His hand is moving slowly under the bar for a gun.

> BEACH
>
> I'm looking for Boots. Think he'd like to see me.

BARMAN nearly has the gun. Beach moves forward and throws a fast punch across the bar. It's a solid hit, sending the barman against the back bar, spilling a row of stacked glasses.

Smiling, he recovers, springing over the bar for the detective, who sidesteps his lunge. The barman sprawls on the floor, grabs Beach's foot and shoves him against the bar rail. He advances. Beach takes out his gun and whips it across the guy's mouth, hitting bone and drawing blood.

> BARMAN
>
> Shouldna done that. Gonna have to take you
> the hard way.

Barman bends and throws a large bucket of ice cubes at Beach, then charges -- tackling him around the waist, crashing onto the bar's wooden floor slats. He pins the detective's face and pours a bottle of liquor into his eyes. Beach

YELLS at the burning effect. He pounds his fist into Beach's stomach and continues pounding.

Beach gropes for the empty bottle, finds it, breaks off the neck and shoves the splintered edge at the barman. It catches the him on the ear -- he SCREAMS wildly. It's a deep bloody gash.

Beach blinks, trying to see, but it's pretty dark and blurred for him. Barman clutches hold of an ice pick and comes down on Beach, moving for him as the detective stumbles back--

BEACH'S POV -- a bluffed, out of focus view of the bartender – advancing.

ANOTHER ANGLE as Beach hits the back wall. The bartender stabs for Beach's face, but the detective turns at the last moment. The pick lands in the wall, just inches from his neck.

Beach jerks his knee into the guy's groin, who GROANS miserably. Beach feels for the pick behind him, finds it, and yanks it out. He puts it into his coat pocket, then shoves the bartender into the men's room where he collapses in one of the urinals. Beach primes a stool against the closed door, and climbs the back stairs for Boots' office.

ANGLE IN BOOTS' OFFICE as Beach enters slowly. It's empty. But he hears something. Something like voices talking.

ANGLE IN HALLWAY as Beach follows the sound. He approaches a door marked PRIVATE. The sound is LOUDER, more distinct. Softly, he cracks the door open and slips in.

ANGLE IN THEATRE as Beach enters from the balcony level. He closes the door quickly, then drops to his knees, letting his eyes adjust to the darkness.

ANOTHER ANGLE as Beach peers cautiously over the ledge and sees on the movie screen an IMAGE that appears to be a 35MM SLIDE of MARILYN FROM THE NUDE SESSION.

There are three men seated below in the center section. A lazy trail of cigar smoke rises, entwining itself in the projected beam of light. The conversation between the men is able to be heard.

The voice of the first man is not recognizable, though it is clear he dominates the other two, who refer to him as JIMMY. The second voice is easily distinctive, belonging to Boots.
ANGLE ON BEACH as he moves down a bit, changing his angle to identify the third individual. It is CRAINE.

Several slides from the nude session appear on the screen.

> CRAINE
> Jimmy, how about that one?

CLOSE ON SCREEN on Marilyn -- with a man's St. Christopher around her neck.

> JIMMY
> Get that baby blown up. Nice and big.

> BOOTS
> Beautiful.

> JIMMY
> Show me the other stuff.

Boots calls up to the projection booth.

> BOOTS
> Advance ahead a few.

ANGLE ON SCREEN where the slides of Marilyn change to a SLIDE of Beach shaking hands with JIM CRAINE. Then the two entering a limousine.

ANGLE ON BEACH peering over the edge watching the slides intently.

NEW SLIDE of Beach stepping out of the limo and entering a beach front home.

                              JIMMY
            That's good. Will people know it's the Lawford's house?

                              CRAINE
            We'll make sure they do.

CRAINE AND BEACH on the sand in front of Lawford's -- an envelope
passing between them.

                              JIMMY
            Good job boys. Nice tie in. The dick was working
            for the Kennedy's, plain and simple.

                              BOOTS
            Look at this next one, Jimmy.

NEW SLIDE of Beach in Monroe's bedroom slumped on the floor to the
body of Marilyn on her bed.

                              JIMMY
            What's the latest from the coroner?

                              CRAINE
            Still nothing official. We used suppositories.
            Back door.

                              BOOTS
            Neal prepped the coroner.

                              JIMMY
            What about prints?

                              CRAINE
            Plenty.

                              BOOTS
            I guess the only thing we have to worry
            about is that goddamn Beach kid on the loose.

CRAINE

That fucking Neal!

Jimmy stands up.

JIMMY

I'll put a contract out on this kid. And the girl.
They've been lucky once too often.
Today, tomorrow, my boys'll find them.

BOOTS

I'll make sure the right people get the pictures.

JIMMY

Do that because the Kennedy's won't
take this lying down.

Puffing his cigar, Jimmy strolls to the side of the theatre and exits.

ON BEACH sneaking down a tiny flight of stairs and moving quietly for the projectionist room. He taps on the door, motioning for the young projectionist to step out.

PROJECTIONIST

What happened?

BEACH

Nothing. Except this.

He points the gun at the projectionist, a frightened anemic sap.

BEACH

So much as a chirp from you, wallflower,
and this gun goes to work. Now, over into
the woman's john.

Beach walks them over to the woman's restroom.

ANGLE INSIDE as Beach motions for the youth to step into a stall, then closes the latch after him.

> BEACH
> Off with the clothes. Pass them over.

One by one the articles come over the stall.

> BEACH
> Stay put. I got a partner won't like it if you try and leave.

Beach leaves, returning to the projection room, looking down. Boots is there alone. Lou looks at the tray of incriminating slides, thinking. He takes out the matches from Roshi, using them to set the slides on fire. As they begin to flame -- a LOUD shriek erupts from the Tunnel Exit -- and within moments Craine emerges -- his arm coiled around Cherie. She squirms fiercely to free herself. Craine drags her over to Boots.

> CRAINE
> I'll tell you why she wasn't home,
> because she was here with Beach.
> Okay doll, where is he?

She doesn't answer. Craine twists her arm sharply.

> CRAINE
> Answer me!

Again, she refuses. Craine whips his hand across her face

> CRAINE
> What are you doing out there?

Silence.

> BOOTS
> Lousy goddamn bitch!

Boots hits her. Cherie falls to her knees, hunches in pain on the floor. Craine tears the back of her dress off.

                         CHERIE
              No...!

Boots unstraps his leather belt and whips it hard across her back. Cherie SCREAMS.

                         CRAINE
              Ready to talk now?

                         CHERIE
              Fuck you both.

Boots bring his belt down stinging across her back.

                         BOOTS
              Next time you get the buckle. Where is he?

Cherie is crying, not answering. Boots turns, looking up at the projection booth.

                         BOOTS
              Oh for Christ's sake! What's the matter with
              the little jerk now!

Craine jerks Cherie to her feet.

                         CRAINE
              You're getting it now -- bitch!

Boots climbs the stairs, advancing on the projection booth.

EXT. SWAMIS - NIGHT

Townes starts inside the bar.

ANGLE INSIDE as he surveys the debris. He's not sure what to do -- but smells something -- burning? -- And moves for the stairs. He climbs up for second floor.

ON BEACH snapping off the projector -- throwing the theatre into blackness. Then he jumps from the ledge down to the aisle below. As he lands, a GUNSHOT is fired. Then another. Cherie SCREAMS. The slide projector suddenly flares back on.

ANGLE ON CHERIE running down the center aisle, near the screen -- silhouetted against a blazing image of Marilyn on the screen -- now in a tight, close up of her smiling face. Craine runs after Cherie.

                    CRAINE
          Stop!

                    BEACH
          Duck Cherie!

ON BOOTS, in the projection room, spots Beach and opens fire. The detective squirms behind a row of seats, firing back.

ON CRAINE firing at Cherie.

CLOSE ON CHERIE running. SHE'S HIT.

ANOTHER ANGLE as she falls against the movie screen -- and lies motionless under the luminous canvas of Marilyn.

ANGLE ON BEACH seeing that she's been hit. Beach fires again up at Boots. The big man GROANS, spilling out and hitting the carpet in a deadening thud.

Beach rises to his feet and fires blindly -- looking for a sign of Craine's whereabouts. He sees nothing and ducks back down behind the seats. Flattening onto his stomach, and begins inching forward. Slowly, he checks across each new row for Craine.

ROW AFTER ROW as he crawls down toward the screen. No Craine.

LAST ROW, near the screen, he sees something move in the corner. Edging a little closer, he notes the gentlest of ruffling through the heavy velvet curtains. He angles over, his gun ready.

ANGLE ON CURTAINS where we can see a man's shoe protruding several inches out -- as if someone were hiding behind. At ten yards off, Beach can't miss and fires into the velvet -- at a spot several feet above the shoe. Quickly, he advances the cartridge forward into an empty chamber, and fires a blank. There is a dull sound -- signifying an empty gun. Nothing happens from the first bullet's impact -- only an echo and a small fluttering of the thick curtains,

ANGLE ON CRAINE emerging from behind some seats on the edge of the aisle nearest the curtains. He approaches Beach, smiling, walking unevenly on his shoeless foot.

> CRAINE
> You're dumber than I thought, falling for
> an old gag like that.

He's feeling cocky, has his gun out, but does not have it aimed.

> BEACH
> Only thing worse is thinking someone would fall for it.

> CRAINE
> (still smiling)
> No, Beach.

> BEACH
> It's not going to work.

> CRAINE
> You wanna bet?

He raises his gun to shoot.

But Beach fires first, putting his last bullet into Craine's foot at the base of the leg. The gun in his hand falls, but his face registers no pain.

ANGLE ON SCREEN as the projector unjams and slide of Marilyn continues, but because of heat -- begins to burn.

ON CRAINE slowly and with effort advancing on Beach. The detective brings out the ice pick and plunges it into Craine's stomach. Jerking backward, Craine knocks Beach's hand away and yanks the blade out of himself. Blood flows from the wound. Beach moves cautiously back -- unable to believe Craine is still on his feet!

                              CRAINE
                          (gasping)
                  Been awhile since I carved a man up,
                  cut up plenty in Korea, plenty.

ON CRAINE - a hideous gleam in his eyes and the ice pick wedged in his grip as he moves on Beach -- forcing him up against the screen, pinned. Craine then lunges the pick at Beach. The blade flashes for his face, barely missing -- tearing instead into the screen -- fracturing the image of Marilyn's face.

ON CRAINE ready to try again. Beach narrowly ducks another scrape, but Craine succeeds in tripping him. On his back, Beach struggles across the stage -- trying to get away.

Craine leaps for him, landing on the detective's shins.

Beach kicks furiously but can't get Craine off. Finally, Craine has him pinned.

CLOSE ON BEACH making every effort to throw Craine off. But he can't.

CLOSE ON CRAINE squeezing at Beach's throat.

CLOSE ON BEACH gasping to breathe, his strength ebbing as he sees Craine raise the ice pick over his head.

ON CRAINE setting to plunge the ice pick.

ON BEACH this is it the end, there's no stopping Craine.

A SHOT RINGS OUT. GUNFIRE, THEN ANOTHER. Craine falls over, collapsing beside Beach, the ice pick still cemented in his grip.

ON BEACH turning to see Townes perched high up in the alcove on the balcony level. Slowly, he lowers his gun.

> TOWNES
> Jesus, it took me forever to get a clear shot
> at the bastard. You all right?

Beach's head falls back, as he gratefully breathes in a couple deep, delicious lungful of air.

> BEACH
> Yeah... I'm fine.

AFTER A MOMENT, Beach gets up and crosses to Cherie.

ON CHERIE -- sprawled on her back, her dress torn.

ON BEACH kneeling beside her, gently feeling for her pulse. She opens her eyes and smiles weakly.

CLOSE ON BEACH trying to contain himself, his emotions.

TENDERLY, he brushes the hair off her forehead and looks at her lovely face. Then up at the torn screen as the image of Marilyn looks down on them.

> BEACH
> Don't die on me, angel.

> CHERIE
> We've still got places to go...

He takes her hand – squeezing it.

CHERIE

...a lot more.

The CAMERA SLOWLY PULLS BACK UP THE AISLE as we leave Lou cradling Cherie in his arms. The torn celluloid image of MARILYN hovering above them.

RUN CREDITS AND CONTINUE TO SLOWLY PULL BACK...

Epilogue: The Final Act

Do not go away.

As mentioned in the prologue, there is still story to tell. Still voices that must speak. Truths that must be heard. Forty years is a long time, and once trickling out, the truth must be allowed to purge itself entirely and run its full course – no matter where it leads.

It is that course and final end-point, the final revelation that must now be recounted.

As mentioned in the prologue, we were quite serious on seeking the manuscript's publication, but we were equally keen on attaching some article of proof supporting the story's veracity. That, in fact, everything Lou Beach had written was true. I wanted something that would silence any cynics who might argue this was just some imaginatively stitched façade of fact and fiction. I wanted an artifact, a piece of the story's real history, tangible and unarguable, that would annihilate all such doubt and corroborate Beach's account irrefutably.

The axiom "Be careful what you wish for" would prove starkly true in our case as we turned our efforts in this regard – stepping into the dark undercurrents, the twisting labyrinth ourselves – moving toward the final layer of deceit to be peeled away and reveal the story's final, brutal truth. A truth so treacherous and truly shocking, I doubt even Beach himself suspected.

The problem of validation, of course, was the time factor. Forty years is a long stretch for such artifacts to disappear permanently. And Beach's own disappearance didn't exactly help the excavation efforts. Still, we tried – succeeding in placing certain people in certain locations that were consistent with Beach's account. But something tangible, like a photograph, a written communication, an item of factual tangency to the story remained elusively beyond our grasp.

And then the announcement that Jackie Onasis' estate was going up for auction at Sotheby's in early 1996.

At first it didn't register with either of us the possible connection. Zhen showed a little more intuitive resource, requesting a catalogue. "You never know," she cited, eagerly scanning the pages of rare Kennedy family memorabilia. I think she may have just contrived this as an excuse to indulge in a little reckless voyeuring into the private world of this very private lady. But it was fascinating. We both sat one evening during cocktails perusing the 584-page catalogue, fascinated by the sheer volume of items. Some strikingly personal, some boringly ordinary. A lot of interesting debris as it were. Nothing seemed particularly connective, Beach to Kennedy, so we had dinner and afterwards finished the catalogue in bed.

Zhen sat up. "Look at item 892, page 12. Under miscellaneous."

I found the item. An unidentified cigar humidor. Damaged. Origin unknown. We both looked at each other, a chill prickling my spine. Zhen had the same look.

"Oh, my God!" we both exclaimed together, knowing immediately what it might mean.

"It couldn't be," I said.

"The one she bought right before -- ."

But we were both thinking: what if it was. The humidor Marilyn had purchased for Bobby that Beach had used to hide the needle before the arrival of the official onslaught.

I called Sotheby's, inquiring about the particular item, if they could at least provide me with the make of the humidor, but was told that would be quite impossible. Thus the decision was made: we'd just have to fly back to New York and attend the auction ourselves.

Along with the mass of others jammed into the Sotheby's hall along 72nd street we made our way in. It was really quite something, the feeding frenzy atmosphere, intensely watchable – the uncertainty of our pursuit more than compensated by the sheer spectacle. Graceland comes to Manhattan. Sotheby's interior had been masterly transformed into something resembling a Japanese department store with it's different thematic collection of rooms. There was a New York section that re-created Jackie's Fifth Avenue apartment; a country section with pieces grouped from the homes in Martha's Vineyard and New Jersey; and of course a White House area with the grand menagerie of items large and small from the Washington years. The crowd was diverse and the dress ranged from hot pink minis to New York black with pearls. But we were vultures, all of us, in different guises.

At last the bidding for our item began. Fortunately, we'd had a chance to preview the piece, without actually examining it, and from our legwork in L.A. knew it was the same make as Marilyn's purchase. With this information and a somewhat sweaty palm clutching the auction paddle, I was prepared to go the distance – within reason. Like most of the other items, bidding soared beyond the catalogue's suggested $100 value. After all, it was damaged. But still there were some devoted enthusiasts, thinking if they couldn't snare the famous JFK humidor this might be a worthy consolation. I was stunned when the gravel concluded its third and final bang – awarding me the humidor for $9,000.

After taking care of payment and procedure, we gleefully whisked our little treasure back to our hotel suite, preferring its privacy for what remained.

"What do you think?" Zhen asked me as the cab crawled sluggishly uptown.

Naturally pensive, I must have been even more so for her to ask. Looking out the window at late afternoon Manhattan, I was thinking how strange life is – how existence is so inter-connected, all those lives out there….the hidden dramas, the untold secrets. And I was somehow trying to think how I would feel when the whole escapade to New York turned out to be one long, wild-goose chase.

"Oh," I sighed, turning to her with a small smile, "just trying to be guardedly optimistic."

"Look, sweetie," Zhen soothed, "even if….it….the needle – isn't, you know – there inside, it's still an incredible story. We'll get it published."

"But do you realize how much more infinitely credible it will be? But Christ, who are we kidding! The odds are just too huge."

"Then let's just do it now," she said. "Let's open it and get it over with."

Which we did.

And as I suspected, found it completely empty. The humidifying element attached to the lid's ceiling Beach had used to stash the needle was gone. Ripped out, hinges and all.

We returned to our hotel suite, less than triumphant. We sat, the humidor between us on the table. Just sitting, thinking. Evening fell. I poured us a drink.

"I'm certain, " Zhen speculated, "that Beach must have somehow contacted someone about it. From Mexico, or wherever he ended up in Asia."

"No doubt," I agreed. "There's no way he wouldn't have gotten word out."

"The whole thing was removed."

"They weren't taking any chances."

"In a way, that kind of corroborates what Beach wrote."

"In a way," I yawned without much enthusiasm.

We had another drink. Thought about dinner. Evening was falling.

"You know what would have been nice," I droled wistfully, "for my dad – that ship's log book of JFK's. He would have enjoyed that," I remarked of the item that had gone off right before the humidor.

"Hey, wait a minute," Zhen began, reaching for the Sotheby's catalogue, "remember – they read a sample entry from the catalogue. Here."

We both read through again the description and answers to the entry headings as they appeared in JFK's own handwriting – destination, date, guests aboard, weather conditions, time of arrival, events to remember, etc.

"Mr. Beach, Lou's father, Ted, was an avid sailor, wasn't he?" Zhen asked.

He was, with a wonderful boat, the Toyon, something of a family treasure that had passed on since Ted's death several years ago.

"So he had the boat back in '62?"

"Yes. So --- ?"

"Beach had to leave the country. Isn't it possible he left by boat? His father's boat? And if he did, maybe it would have been recorded in the ship's log. Like this one."

I thought about it carefully. Actually, it made remarkable sense. It would make the perfect exit, by sea. As undetectable as one could wish for.

A quick call to Michael Beach confirmed that Teddy Beach like all serious boatmen, had indeed faithfully kept a log for his outings on the Toyon for some twenty years. Would these be available to study – specifically for 1962?

Indeed they were, handsomely collected and stored at the Los Angeles Yacht Club – gifted by Teddy Beach to the club of which he had been a member nearly all of his adult life. Located in San Pedro, the club overlooks the marina where many of its members keep their boats. Zhen and I were greeted and, as arranged, shown into the club's small but well tended library. Going through the volumes, we found the one devoted to 1962, Anxiously, we leafed through Teddy Beach's well-written accounts of his summer outings: trips to Catalina mostly, his annual fishing party to Cabo San Lucas. All were dated and logged with a casual kind of precision, informal but thoroughly consistent. Each volume had a numerical page count of 200. On page 96, July 1962, there had been a trip to Avalon with some people from Nicholas Beach Inc. They stayed for one night. Dined at Scari's restaurant. The sail going home was "blessed with a fine afternoon westerly." The next outing for the Toyon was August 12, 1962 – a weekend at Howland's Landing cove with his wife and friends, the Adams. The entry appeared on page 100.

Page 98. Where was it? Whatever outing it logged, occurred between July 30 and August 12. Beach's departure from L.A. most certainly would have been on August 6, or shortly thereafter.

We scanned through other volumes, checking if other specific pages had been extracted, perhaps for some unknown sentimental value. But all volumes proved to be invariably intact – with all pages accounted for.

The only missing page was the one from the week in August. Very, very strange. The coincidence was too much: sometime in that first week of August 1962, the Toyon had gone somewhere, that was for whatever reasons, unsuitable to remain recorded in the ship's log.

"I believe," Zhen said, "that's known in today's vernacular as `hitting the delete button'."

Studying the other entries at some length, I noticed a recurring name who wasn't family or, I surmised, a business associate. The name Arnie was an almost certain entry among the "Guests Aboard" line, appearing on every outing the Toyon made that year.

The question was soon enough posed to Michael Beach.

"Oh, yeah – Arnie. Uncle Ted's Swedish boatman. One-eyed Arnie. Took care of the Toyon for at least a decade. God, I haven't thought of Arnie in years. Wonder whatever happened to him?"

So did we, and set immediately to finding out.

Postscript 2

"He was no saint, and he could swear like a sonofabitch when things weren't done right. But he was the best man – bar none, that I ever had the privilege of crewing for."

Arnie Bergman looked at us with his one good eye, finished his first beer and excused himself after offering this assessment of Teddy Beach to make a phone call.

There is a book store in San Pedro on sixth street that stocks along with it's fiction and non-fiction titles, a wide variety of foreign language newspapers – catering to the many merchant marine crewmen off the international cargo ships putting into the port town. If you want an Italian, French, Japanese, or Swedish daily you go to William's Book Store.

And, in our case, if you want to track down an aging one-eyed Swedish boatman, William's isn't a bad place to start either. So we were directed from the L.A. Yacht Club.

San Pedro is a small town, with a predominance of people who make their living one way or another on or around the sea. And with its geographic insularity – surrounded by water on three sides, the law of separation reduces down to three or four people in San Pedro. Jerry at Williams Books didn't know an Arnie, but he did have a regular Swede customer in Arnie's age range of 60-70, and a few phone calls during the next two days brought us to the Upper Deck bar and grill having beers with Arnie, Teddy Beach's boatman for so many years.

"So anyway," Arnie continued on his return, "when Mr. Ted called that morning saying to fuel the boat, get it ready, and to meet his son Lou at noon – I didn't think twice. Whatever Mr. Ted wanted. I knew Lou a little. He'd been on the boat a number of times, mostly for weekends to Catalina. But he had a weak stomach, got sick easily. Didn't exactly take after his old man. So it kind of surprised me when I got the call that morning – to meet Lou at the Toyon at noon."

"And that's all – just to meet him at noon? You didn't know where he would want to go? Didn't know if he was in trouble or anything?"

"I didn't know anything. Just got the boat ready. Lou showed up at noon, by himself. Had on a wrinkled suit, looked like he'd slept in it, and a bag of some new clothes, casual stuff. We got underway, just the two of us. Weather was typical summer. Being the middle of the day, a little westerly was blowing, giving the water a light chop. Lou mixed a couple bloody marys for himself, I think the alcohol helped his stomach, got him to relax. He slept below for a couple hours. Woke up around Oceanside. Made some tuna sandwiches. Talked some."

"What'd you talk about?"

"What did we talk about?" Arnie repeated thoughtfully, "we talked about religion. About the Buddha. He had some strange ideas. Then we listened to the news. I remember there was a lot about the actress Marilyn

Monroe who had died."

"Did he mention anything about that?"

"No. But he did seem pretty keen on it, if I remember. Listened a lot. Then, later, about 7:00, we turned on the Dodger game. Docked for gas in San Diego. Bought some beer, few other things. We made Ensanada about 6:00 in the morning."

"And that's where you left him?"

"Yes. That's where he got off. Ensanada, Mexico."

"And he still hadn't told you anything?" Why? Or if something was wrong. Nothing?"

"Not a word. I figured if he wanted me to know, he'd tell me. If not, then it wasn't any of my business."

"So you dropped him off and returned to L.A.?"

"Yes."

"How did the page get missing? From the log. Did you take it?"

"No. I think it was the other guy."

"What other guy?"

"I don't know him. Not really. And I never told Mr. Ted. I just call him the other guy. A week or so after I got back, this guy was kind of hanging around the marina. We chatted a little, just being polite. Then one afternoon we had a beer and he was curious about the Toyon. Or he seemed to be. One day he asked if he could take a look inside. So I said okay. No big deal. Boat people are curious about other boats, their design, how much room they got below. That sort of thing."

"So he came on board – and ---?"

"And I don't know for sure, but I think when I wasn't looking he checked the log and took the page out. I just had this feeling he was pretending to be boat interested – for another reason. You work around boats long enough and you get a sense for people – if they're boat people or not. He was not boat. But he was good, very good, at pretending."

"What did the entry say?"

"Just exactly what happened. San Pedro to Ensanada. Lou, myself."

"Nothing else? Did you make any comments?"

"No. But -- ."

"Yes?"

Arnie rubbed his chin, trying to make up his mind. He finished his second beer, signaling to the waitress for another. "Oh, hell! I guess it's okay to tell. So long ago. And Mr. Ted's dead."

We waited for Arnie to continue. His eye watching a large tanker slowly passing us – making its way down channel toward the breakwater.

"Right before he left, in Ensanada, Lou asked me to keep something – that wasn't really his, but he was a little leery of having on him."

"What?"

"An envelope that had a man's passport and a one-way ticket to Havana."

Zhen and I looked at each other, as the waitress set the new beer down.

"His?"

"No. Not Lou's. Somebody else's. Somebody he said wouldn't be needing it anymore, but Lou didn't want to ditch it."

"So he wanted you to keep it for him?"

"Until he contacted me. And he didn't want me mentioning it to Mr. Ted. No one. Just hang onto it, he said, and be careful."

"So that's why you think this other guy may have been sniffing around?"

"Yes. So I took it from my home and put it in a safety deposit box at my bank And, I'm not certain, but pretty sure – someone was in my home. Nothing taken, but there were just little things off."

"The guy broke in – searching?"

"Seemed like."

There was a long moment of silence, each of us pondering this.

"Do you still have them – the passport and ticket?" I asked.

He studied us for a long beat. Then slowly nodded and sighed. "I guess I always knew someone sometime would ask me about them. Yes. They're safe."

More silence. I watched Arnie, looking down at his shoes – old, worn Topsider's, tapping against the wooden plankboards of the deck.

"What's going on?" Arnie asked, "I mean – what's this really all about?" He only had one eye, but he could make that into a drilling force all by itself.

We told him, ordering a couple appetizers and more beer.

"So that's it! Jesus," he exclaimed when we were through. "I always wondered. Never dared asked Mr. Ted directly – just vaguely wondered what Lou was doing. And he'd always answer Lou was fine, living in Japan. Mr. Ted wouldn't say much beyond that. But I could tell he missed him. Missed him a lot....I remember one trip we all took to Catalina. Lou, of course, was sick. Just miserable. Over the side the entire trip. And each time he heaved into the ocean, Mr. Ted tightened his stomach. I think it hurt him, hearing his son like that. He really wanted Lou to enjoy sailing. But he just couldn't. And then disappearing like he did."

It was evening with the lights of the harbor just beginning to come on. We enjoyed the view sipping our drinks, nibbling the last of the food. Then, very simply, he removed an envelope from his jacket and pushed it across the table to us.

"I've had them long enough. Why don't you two keep them now. I remember your Uncle, Jack O'Melveny. He and Mr. Ted had some good times on the Toyon. I liked him. My eye didn't bother him like some people. So I suppose they'll be safe with you. Anyway, I'm getting too old."

"You're sure?"

"It's a relief. After Mr. Ted passed on, I didn't really know what to do. Now I do. There's also this leather eyeglass holder. It was empty but part of what Lou gave me. Might as well take it, too."

We did, thanking him, saying we'd be in touch and driving back the 110 freeway for home to better examine our potential artifacts.

Postscript 3

The name on the passport and the one-way ticket to Havana was Mejas Recinaski. There was nobody even remotely close to such a name appearing in Beach's story. Who was this individual? How had such documents come into Beach's possession? And why had he considered them so valuable?

I was for hitting the sack and letting our sub-conscious go to work, but Zhen had other ideas. She wanted to make a pot of coffee, put on some Miles Davis and ponder what we'd received. I said good night as "Kinda Blue" started whispering its classic lines.

Sometime in the middle of the night Zhen roused me excitedly.

"I think I have something. This Mejas Recinaski. I was getting nowhere so I worked a little on last Sunday's crossword puzzle (NY Times, every Sunday, religiously) And it hit me – try unscrambling the letters."

I looked at her, thinking what in the hell….

Mejas Recinaski --- Mejas spells out to James. And Recinaski – minus the ethnic `ski' letters out to Craine."

"James Craine," I gasped, now fully awake.

Zhen's eyes lit triumphantly: "Jim Craine. Exactly!"

"Craine was leaving the country under an alias. That's rather interesting."

We thought about that, about Craine. I looked at the picture on the passport and saw immediately the match in Beach's description from the story.

"But think about it – considering what had happened – Craine had blown his cover with the Kennedys, so it's hardly surprising."

"Except Craine couldn't have figured on being exposed like that. It's a little excessive - planning a departure like that."

"True."

We thought some more about Craine.

"But," I countered, "if Beach had been picked up at Marilyn's as they'd planned, would Craine have gone on at the Lawford's – business as usual?"

"It would have looked awfully suspicious for him to disappear. There was really no tying Craine to any of the conspirators."

"But, on the other hand, maybe he just figured – obvious or not, what difference does it make. The job's done – and it's time to get the hell out of Dodge."

"But Cuba? Seems odd."

"Didn't the mob have ties down there? Trafficante, Giancana?"

"Yeah. Actually, it wouldn't be a bad place to hole up for awhile."

"Drink a couple Cuba libres."

"Smoke some Havana's."

"Take a course or two on Communism."

"Watch Kennedy sweat it out over Marilyn – explaining why a private dick he hired was found in her bedroom that night."

"Wait for the CIA to come barking."

"Anyway," I said lowering myself back into bed, "however you slice it, Craine was bailing and Arnie's story makes a nice little book-end to Beach's exit. Think we should mention it – a little epilogue to the screenplay?"

"I wonder," Zhen said inspecting the passport – holding it up to the light, "if there's a way to tell if this is forged."

"Look for the Valley Forge Printer's logo," I joked.

"Very funny," she continued looking. "But what about this."

"Good lord, what now?"

"Maybe nothing. But...then again..."

She showed me the passport. A small dot, perhaps the size of a large period, had slipped from the sheet, but had caught in the creased fold.

"What do you suppose?"

"I dunno," I answered, as we both squinted at it.

Zhen went to fetch the small magnifying glass we sometimes use for very fine print. Holding it close, she peered at the small dot.

"I'm not sure, but there's some kind of very fine marking."

"Writing?"

"It's hard to tell. Maybe. Here, take a look."

It was very difficult, but there were definitely some minutely small etchings.

"God – do you think it could be, like, some kind of secret communiqué?" Zhen wondered.

We let that thought filter through several layers of possibility.

"Like some kind of reduced, micro-dot photography," I speculated.

We both looked at each other.

Some more mental filtering.

"Very covert stuff," Zhen said.

"Very."

We wondered.

Maybe it was.

Maybe it wasn't.

"We have to get it enlarged," Zhen suggested.

"First thing," I agreed.

So there it was – a small, micro-dot with perhaps miniaturized writing some kind of secret communication from forty years ago. Was this our artifact?

✳ ✳ ✳ ✳ ✳ ✳ ✳

That morning I called Robert, my art friend from college. Robert would know what to do. He had a darkroom and vast equipment. He is my oracle on all things regarding photography and reproduction. I told him what I had, withholding the factual particulars, asking could he help.

"I'll take it over to Stephen at Kodak on Las Palmas," he said cheerily.

"You can't do it?"

"No way. This is real technical stuff. Needs a very specific camera.

But Stephen should be okay. How small did you say it was?"

I told him and he went through the operation and developing, saying with some luck and Kodak not being too busy it might possibly be done by afternoon.

"Can we trust this guy Stephen?"

"Yeah, he's cool."

"Tell him to be discreet."

"Discreet – like he could get in trouble?"

"No, discreet like just have him do it, keep his mouth shut and get it back to us as quickly and quietly as possible."

✶✶✶✶

We had it back by 5:00. A half column from the L.A. Times Classified in August 1962. One of the ads was circled in black pen, reading:

> The Lord Jesus died for your sins.
> Gravity speaks. The rock falls in the
> Ocean. Who among you will cast the
> First stone? Who will save your soul?

Twenty-eight words. Five sentences. None of it making any sense contextually. We were depressed, unable to make any connection whatsoever to Craine or Kennedy or Marilyn. I'll spare you the plethora of questions we concocted trying to fathom a shred of meaning in something that had so obviously been meant – by its covert reduction – to convey something of vital importance.

It had to be a code. Between two people. Craine and whomever. There was no other possible explanation.

But what exactly did that mean? Who used codes?

"Agents and operatives. Sneaky people," Zhen answered.

"But why – Let's backtrack. The final scene. At Swamis. They're going over everything. Pictures. Frame-up. What they have and how they're going to nail the Kennedys. Everything out in the open. Face to face. The done deal"

"So who was Craine linked with that they needed to communicate thru this kind of covert system?"

"Which would mean a relationship with someone beyond the conspirators – that had to remain hidden."

"And maybe that's why the person broke into Arnie's house – after taking the page from the log – something of Craine's that needed to stay covered."

"Yes!" I high-fived her. "Good." I felt chills along my spine. "Are you beginning to think there's more?"

"More?"

"That Jim Craine or Mejas Recinaski or whoever the hell he is --- ."

"Was," Zhen corrected.

"Don't be cute….that this guy wasn't who we thought he was."

"Or that Beach thought he was."

Zhen picked up the eye-glass holder. "Or, for that matter. What might be hidden inside this harmless case."

"Yeah, right. Don't go overboard on this stuff," I continued, enjoying her sense of play.

"Not over – under. Underneath." And fishing for a small pairing knife from the pantry, she slit the case open.

And out spilled two slightly off-white tablets and a hard, plastic security/clearance type card.

Postscript 4

Five days later, some major favors – who in turn pulled their own strings for us, we had our answers.

The pills, after lab analysis, were cyanide. Not manufactured in the U.S.

The plastic card was a temporary-issue clearance to a certain sector of the CIA Headquarters in Virginia used during those years.

The passport in Mejas Recinaski's name had been checked also and the opinion was that it was too good not to have been done at government level. "This is as good as it gets," came the finding.

I'm not sure if utter incredulity is the right emotion for what these discoveries did to us. Maybe pure shock – but with a certain dangerous thrill. We were literally approaching a kind of precipice – a chasm where our previously held interpretation of the murder conspiracy rendered by Beach was becoming incomplete: Craine's involvement extended possibly to the CIA.

That possibility was not a little imposing for our having stumbled upon it – and almost certainly being the only ones possessing that knowledge. Imagining Craine connected to the CIA and the existence of a rogue element within the government body scheming to assassinate Monroe in an attempt to eventually eliminate a disfavored President was darkly impacting.

But, as Beach himself quoted the Attorney General during their initial interview at the Lawford's: "There are some pretty dedicated men on the other side who will do just about anything to insure their side's victory next election…there's no telling where this might end up once I bring in a sector of the security machine." His desire to keep the matter a private one, now in hindsight, seems prophetically warranted and a shrewdly realistic appraisal of the workings of his own government. Trust no one.

Shocking as it seems, Craine's alleged connection to the CIA would explain crucial points: the enduring, decades-long cover-up that has effectively buried this truth from surfacing, a cover-up that has destroyed files, altered evidence, and silenced testimony. The case stays shut and mired in innuendo because elements in the government want it that way.

It would certainly explain the strategy of using Hoffa, turning him into the perfect shield in deflecting any damaging collusion rumors from arising by virtue of his own bitter feud to destroy Kennedy.

And perhaps most importantly it would explain how Craine's clearance and placement in such a high-level security position, that of guarding the President's sister, which would have undoubtedly been subject to a grueling background check, could have been accepted. It would be difficult to imagine someone from Hoffa's ranks passing through such a rigorous screening process.

All in all, upon reflection, there were substantial elements and logic to believe Craine's association with the CIA.

It must be further added there is ample evidence of the CIA's own rage against the Kennedys that would more than provide a motivation for what was attempted. During the embarrassing and badly handled Bay of Pigs debacle in 1961, the CIA felt Kennedy vacillated inexcusably at the moment of crisis by refusing air strikes and armed forces intervention – leaving the 1,500 Cuban exiles floundering dangerously on the beaches against Castro's well-armed defenders. Though Kennedy publicly accepted full responsibility, the Agency felt he had betrayed their efforts, and the ensuing acrimony left a permanent scar. And when Kennedy learned of the Agency's direct violation of his orders by directing CIA operatives onto the beaches, he privately declared he'd like "to splinter the CIA into a thousand pieces and scatter them to the wind." The Agency was more and more in those years pursuing its own, private agenda with a determined arrogance.

Hoffa, of course, needs no accounting for his personal vendetta against Bobby Kennedy. To the question of collusion between Hoffa and the Agency one only has to consider Operation Mongoose – the Agency's code name for its plan to eliminate Castro. Quite simply, in 1961, the Agency had determined its own efforts to assassinate the Cuban leader were in need of more seasoned, professional assistance and turned to the mob. Havana, pre-Castro, had been a gold mine to the underworld, who were more than eager to lend a hand in disposing of Castro to bring back the old days. Though these efforts, which included food poisoning at one of Castro's favorite restaurants, poison pills, explosives, detonators, etc. – were not successful, the collaboration is well documented and would easily establish a precedent for the Agency to consider conspiring with Hoffa. They did it once, they'd do it again – especially given the time factor 1961-1962. It's how they were thinking in those days.

Our attempts to reference a Jim Craine or Mejas Recinaski with the Agency or any other government branch all came back negligible. Not surprising. As were all other inquiries regarding his employment with the Lawfords. Craine, as far as the government was concerned, was virtually persona non-grata.

Given what we know now about the JFK assassination, that it was almost certainly the work of a conspiring group within the government and intelligence network that tentacled out to organized crime figures, is it not equally plausible a similar design and collaboration was brought to bear on a vulnerable, romantically distraught and emotionally hurting Hollywood actress?

Was Lou Beach the `Oswald' of this preliminary "Get-Kennedy" effort?

Was the Monroe episode a warm-up, a dress rehearsal for Dallas?

Which brings us now to the mysteriously worded communiqué in the L.A. Times.

$$\star\star\star\star\star$$

It was a shot in the dark, a whistle in the wind, a hopelessly frail wish, but I did it anyway, simply because there was nothing else to do. I placed an ad, just as it was – with a phone number, exactly back in the classifieds where it had originally run.

I don't play the Lotto. I will occasionally wager on the ponies in the summer in Del Mar. I hate Vegas. Gaming talk and issues of point spreads are Greek to me. Meeting Zhen was 10,000-1. Getting her to fall in love a minor miracle. So right there alone I'm tapped out in my allotment of long shots coming in.

Still what else was there. Nothing. There was only trying. So I placed it for a month at $55.72. The last week would be on August 5 – the anniversary of Marilyn's death. I bold headlined it with: MEJAS RECINASKI. That and the proximity of the running date were my only shafts of hope, my only beacons of light to guide a pair of eyes to this signal from the past. Would that silent but knowledgeable conspirator of Craine's still be on alert?

It took forever, the waiting. The waiting of no reply. The waiting of silence. Watching for a shooting star that never appears.

How ridiculously silly of us to expect anything.

Surely.

Nearly forty years ago. What were we thinking.

Then the Sunday, call it fate, miracle – whatever, but there was a reply. A number to call back, which I did, immediately.

"I've been waiting for you," the caller said after I identified myself. "When is the meeting?"

"What -- ?"

"Your ad said there was a meeting to save souls. I want to come. I want to join. I need to be saved. When will it be, please?"

I replied there was no such meeting.

"Oh, then, I'm terribly sorry. Can you at least recommend a meeting?"

"No, I can't."

"I see. Then one last request. Can you direct me where I might purchase a black bike– from Paris?"

Crank, I thought, hanging up, bitterly disappointed, wondering what hole he crawled out of.

Precisely twenty-four hours later, the crank called back. "Well, then, if you can't recommend a bike, can you at least tell me a little something about Jim Craine?"

My heart stopped. "I was hoping you might be able to tell me."

Silence.

"That all depends," the voice said, in a slow, deliberate way that was now different from the crank-call impersonation.

"Yes --?" I urged.

"I can't be a millimeter off."

"What's that?"

"Neither can you. What is your interest in Jim Craine?"

"I discovered something I believe may belong to him."

"How do you even know him?"

"I don't."

"Then why?"

"August. 1962. Marilyn Monroe."

Silence. Although I could clearly sense the caller thinking deeply.

"May I ask to whom I am speaking?"

I told him my name.

"Are you an American citizen?"

"Yes. I was born in Los Angeles."

"You will fax me a copy of your and your father's birth certificates, showing the seal. If all is well, perhaps a meeting can be arranged."

"Yes, I suppose I can do that, but why? Why birth certificates?"

"We can't be off. Not one millimeter."

✶✶✶✶✶

Of course I did as he asked, though badgering my father for a copy of his birth certificate with accompanying explanation was not exactly strainless.

Two days later, on August 3, he called again. This time a meeting was set. The Miramar Sheraton on Ocean Avenue in Santa Monica.

"I know it, " I confirmed.

"In the lobby. 4:00."

"How will I know you?"

"I'll find you," and he hung up.

The next day. The Miramar – one of Santa Monica's more stately hotels is primely located along busy Ocean Avenue atop the Palisades overlooking the Pacific Ocean – several blocks north of the pier. It is a preferred choice of visiting Europeans and New Yorkers wishing for class and elegance near the sea. I like the Miramar. In my early years out of college I lived a block away and would sometimes walk over for a drink after work. I loved watching the barman on busy nights – a real symphony of style handling the volume he did, a truly gifted performance.

I found my way into the lobby, and chose a seat I felt would provide a suitable vantage point to observe the flow of guests in and out.

By 4:15, no one had approached me. I rose, thinking I'd catch a cup of coffee when the lobby's inter-com sounded.

"Would a Don O'Melveny please come to the concierge's desk."

I stopped, listening to my name repeated, making sure, and then headed in that direction.

I presented myself to the concierge who directed me to his desk's phone – as there was a call for me.

"Hello, this is Don."

The voice. "Sorry I've detained you. But I needed to know you were alone."

"Yes of course I'm alone. But where are you?"

"I'm here."

I turned facing the busy lobby, searching among the many passing guests.

"Where?"

"Not now. Tomorrow morning. 10:00. Do you know the Sorrento parking lot along the beach? It's almost directly across from the hotel."

"Yes. I know the lot."

"In the men's room – taped behind the trash container will be a cassette tape. Listen to it."

"Isn't this all a bit excessive," I complained.

"No. You will understand. Because we can't be off. Not even a millimeter. Bring your umbrella."

"Why on earth --- ?"

"Because it might be wet." And he hung up.

Very frustrated, I stared across the busy lobby but still couldn't spot anyone that might be my caller.

I left, driving home, my eyes very much preoccupied on the rear-view mirror.

✷✷✷✷✷

At dinner.

Zhen said: "He's testing."

"But why!? I run an art gallery for God's sake!"

"Yes, but remember – this is some very old, very dangerous business going on."

"The man has to be in his seventies. How much of a threat is that?"

"Maybe he is. But you don't know about the others."

"There are no others."

"We don't know that. There is a crack here in all this. A crack in the whole thing and things are beginning to spill out and you're putting yourself right in its path."

But if he's testing, if he's being so careful – what does that tell you? He's scared. He's coming from a position of weakness."

"Exactly. He's scared. Because there are forces still at play. That haven't died for forty years. And this guy knows it. And he knows more than we do. So if he's scared, I'd say that's a pretty good sign we should be a little nerved, too."

Of course she was right. But I had to press on. By not showing and dealing with this cautious, nameless man who was certainly putting me through some hoops, I would more than likely be forfeiting the final piece to this extraordinary puzzle. So, despite the degree of danger, we both agreed we wanted a complete whole rather than an unfinished near-masterpiece.

We wanted closure.

So, at 10:00, I was there, the Sorrento parking lot of Santa Monica beach – with the umbrella as directed. Years and years ago, there used to be a grill there for breakfast and lunch, but now it had been replaced by some condo units done in gray and white, a kind of Nantucket design. I parked and looked around.

Very innocent. No sign of any ghosts, circa 1962. I climbed out of the car, and moved toward the restroom.

Scared as hell.

Zhen was posted up on the Palisades, at the Miramar, connected by our cellular phones. Help was just a dial away.

Still.

Dark, wet, and stinky, but tolerable and empty, I found the tape. Ripped it clear and lurched quickly out.

Parking lot still empty. Traffic flowed on PCH. The day moved on. Normalcy. Me with a tape scooting for the safety of my car. Inside, I popped it into the deck and hit the door locks.

A man's voice came on. His. "Don't you realize how terribly dangerous it is going into an untested, confined site such as that restroom? No.

203

I suppose you don't. Thank God. I'm up top looking down at you thru binoculars. The park along the bluff. I'm wearing gray flannels and a blue blazer. Reading a Racing Form."

Dialing Zhen for this update, I zoomed up to the Palisades, and parked along the slender peninsula of grass that runs along Ocean Avenue. I meandered through the passing parade of joggers and strollers until spotting the bench and him, peacefully absorbed in the Racing Form. Sensing my approaching presence, he glanced up and smiled pleasantly.

"Thank you for coming. Do – please sit down."

"Thank you. Any winners today?" I asked lightly, nodding to the racing sheets.

"Oh, yes. There are always winners. Whether or not I am fortunate to choose them ---- " he finished with a shrug. He removed his sunglasses, and regarded me rather straight forwardly. As I did him. He had a plain, somewhat pointed face, an intelligent bearing, clean shaven – no evidence of nicks from wobbly hands. Nails were trimmed nicely. His face wore a lifetime of wrinkles, hard ones and soft ones, though the combined effect was not one of remorse. His eyes however, were undoubtedly his most striking element – alive, darting, intensely vigilant.

I had to be sure, you understand," he said, with an air of apology. "Had to be."

"Sure of what?"

"That you weren't one of them."

"One of whom?"

"The people who would like to kill me. Who have been hunting me these forty years. Who are still hunting. The KGB."

Postscript 5

He paused, quietly reading my reaction. I'm not sure what he saw, which quadrant of shock my expression had shifted to, everything felt rather numb.

"My name is Yuri Dovanovitch. I hope you can understand my great caution. I had to be absolutely sure about you."

"But why – the KGB…why are they after you?"

"Because in their eyes I am a traitor. Worst of the worst. A betrayer." He glanced toward the ocean, squinting slightly, his eyes searching the blue expanse. "Because I defected. It is actually quite remarkable I am still alive."

"You are a spy?"

"A rather old fashioned word, but yes – I was trained as a KGB agent. And sent here."

"When did – you defect?"

He looked at me. "How much time do you have?"

"I'm fine."

"You don't have to rush off to anywhere so soon?"

"No."

He nodded. "Then we can talk. I would like to talk. I have been waiting a long time for this. That is the other reason I had to be sure. About you. If you were the one I could tell. I am old. Very old. I want someone to know. Do you believe in fate?"

"Yes," I smiled, "I suppose I do."

"Then would you mind please, before I begin, tell me how fate brought us together on this bench overlooking the ocean. It is important for me to know and I would be grateful."

I related how it had all occurred, the finding of the manuscript, Beach's story, and recovering the remains of Craine's possessions from Arnie.

"I think," Yuri said after I was done, "this Mr. Beach has written accurately. It fills in some blanks for me – about what happened,"

"Then it is all true?"

"Oh, yes. And I can appreciate what he was forced to do, his leaving. It is a long time to be disappeared."

"I guess you would know."

"Although his hunters I'm sure have long given up. Mine – no. Until I die, which won't be long, I will remain a traitor to my homeland. And traitors are dealt with quite harshly. There is a saying we have – when you join the KGB, you are taken care of for life. Leave the KGB – and you are also taken care of – for life."

I nodded, getting the drift.

"And permit me to say this, but you would not make a very good operative," he smiled. "Lucky for us, that's good. You violated very basic trade craft."

"Trade craft --?" I wondered.

"Yes. The mechanics of espionage. What everyone learns. To stay alive."

"Oh."

"You failed with flying colors. An agent would never answer a public page like you did in the Miramar. Too many eyes have seen you."

"You were testing me."

"Of course. And one would never use a hotel phone to discuss arrangements of an assignment. If there was a problem, you would use a `safe' phone. A pay phone. Hotel phones are easily traced. No, never. And you would never walk into a blind – at the beach."

"The restroom?"

"Lethal. No telling who may have been waiting for you. Perfect for the `wet affair'."

"Sorry --?"

"Russian – for assassination."

"Ahhh....and you even tipped me with the line to bring an umbrella – I might get wet."

"And you still walked right into it."

"You really believe after all this time, because you defected, they're still trying to find you?"

"Unfortunately, yes. Not as hard as in the first ten years. But still, yes. There is a book the KGB publishes each year listing all the defectors they still would like to hit. Because they know we are probably giving information to the U.S. government to be used against them. Once a traitor, always a traitor. And traitors are not tolerated by my homeland. They are hunted."

"May I ask why you defected?"

"Because I was no longer able to stand what my country was doing. What I was a part of. It was treachery out of control. Absolutely monstrous. The worst part was leaving my family behind. Never being able to see them again. That was unbearable..."

"Do you have any idea how they are?"

"None. I had no link, no source of knowing. Eventually, I forced myself to divorce my wife so that she would be free to continue her life. Everything had to be eliminated. Severed totally. Any possible connection might be a trail they could use to find me. They are relentless. And I have never allowed myself the luxury of not remembering this. I was once one of them. So I know. I do not believe in all the years I have ever really had a pure night of sleep. And I am tired. I am tired my God of having to eat in restaurants with my back against the wall. I am tired of using protective coloration disguises when I'm out in public. I am tired of having to move every year. Always looking out. Staying alert. So you see, that was how I saw it – your ad. It was an old habit, another check I would just do. Always watching out. That link to the past that maybe they would use to draw me out."

"But what was it?"

"The ad -- ? Instructions for a drop. Very ordinary, communicating like that. We worked with as little personal meeting as possible."

"So you knew Craine?"

"Oh, yes. Very well. I recruited him."

"What is that?"

"One of the KGB's main efforts goes into recruitment of Americans – penetrating important institutions of government and society. It is probably the highest art of Soviet espionage. Without recruitment, an operation is impossible. With it, everything begins."

"You're saying – getting U.S. citizens to work with you in sensitive areas?"

"Yes. Sometimes the contact is made and nurtured solely on the basis of proximity. That is, one day it is hoped the individual will be in a favored position. Sometimes it takes years. Sometimes it never comes to bear."

"But it did with Craine?"

"Yes. Although it certainly took some help. It is rare that someone comes along willingly."

"Why Craine?"

"The case on Craine started in '59. He was involved in some occasional security work for the then Mrs. Lawford, the President's sister. We didn't know if he would be elected, but Craine was targeted on the hope that if Kennedy were elected and he became a full-time staffer for the sister in Los Angeles, it would be an excellent opportunity."

"They think that far in advance?"

"Most Americans are truly naïve about the KGB – how determined they can be. The kind of prospecting that goes on. In Craine's case, the speculation paid off handsomely. But not without considerable planning. This is the other part of recruitment. Where I came in."

He sneezed, pausing to clear his nose, taking out a handkerchief. I studied his clothes – well-pressed gray flannels, button down blue Oxford shirt, shoes polished, front and back. It seemed his life comfortably in tact.

"May I ask you something?"

He nodded.

"Why are you telling me all this? Isn't it....rather unnecessarily risky?"

"I probably shouldn't. But there is a part of me that secretly has been hoping for this chance. I'm old, with a year or two of living perhaps. When I defected, I told the FBI everything, they know my past, what I was involved in. But I believe this should get out for people to know. Otherwise it will lay buried in their file for fifty more years before becoming available. I didn't defect to remain silent. It's important for people to know the truth. That's the big difference between my homeland and here. The truth gets told. It may take awhile. It may not be easy. But it gets told! And you should never take that for granted. That's why I am here. Here with you. Because I always kept hoping, somehow – someone would one day come along, with a good heart, whom I could trust. Someone who wouldn't judge, but would listen to my story, my truth. Someone like me who wanted the story finally told. Because it was all so tragic. And terribly wrong. You understand a little – what I am saying?"

"Certainly."

"But – getting back to Craine, the recruitment process. What happens is finding a person's weak point. Their Achilles' heel. Some way of compromising them. In the KGB it is known as MICE – money, ideology, compromise, and ego. Almost certainly one of these four will be the key. Frequently it is money. Sexual entrapment is often used. Sometimes people are bitter and disillusioned with the government for one reason or another and can enjoy a sense of retribution. But in all cases, recruitment begins with that casual first meeting that will slowly develop into something more. Friendship, then a level of trust, and slowly the enticement will be dangled."

How did you meet Craine?

"The races, out at Santa Anita. Just in line together, waiting our turn to place our bets. We started talking. Just real casual at first. But I made sure we 'bumped' into each other on a fairly regular basis. That's how it begins. One guy to another. Little by little things come out. And I started to figure out who this guy is inside and what he wants. That's what I'm fishing for – his dream."

"What was Craine's?"

"Craine was not happy, he was very unfulfilled. He saw himself as a glorified lacky. A servant. Someone on the sidelines – off stage. Waiting on others. And he didn't want that. He wanted more. He wanted his own power. He had ideas, he would tell me. Big ideas. And one day....."

Yuri turned, looking at me, reading my eyes for understanding.

"This city," he said in a kind of lament, "is so corruptible. Everyone is after something more. The actresses, the actors, all the movie people – everyone. And in a way, Craine was no different. Wanting to be somebody else. Everyone wants their grandeur, don't they?"

I nodded.

"Well, once I learned some of this, I reported back my opinion Craine represented an excellent prospect and I was told to proceed. I didn't push anything, but I maintained the on-going track meetings, with an occasional dinner afterwards."

"So he was trusting you?"

"No. Not yet. That was the next step. But during dinner, after a couple drinks, he'd tell me a little about his job. Working for the Lawfords. What it was like when the President and Attorney General were there. He mostly confided in the social goings-on. Telling me he hated the way he was treated. Said the Kennedys were the biggest snobs. They were very cruel to the staff. He had very harsh feelings about that. And I would sympathize with him. I even told him I had a brother-in-law who was a Cuban exile and how awful the Kennedy's had been during the whole Bay of Pigs fiasco."

"And Craine now, had no idea you were a Russian?"

"Of course not. My English was good. I had a detailed legend, what we call our created histories. All very carefully worked out. I was employed as an accountant for a jewelry company at the time. But I had names and dates, places and people going back ten years that I could talk about – just as if I'd lived here. There was no suspicion. None. To him I was just a somebody he bumped into at the track."

"Was Craine married?"

"No. And that was another thing I put to use. He had a thing for – how should I put this – less than virtuous women."

"Call girls?"

"No. But women who were easy. Maybe needful is a better word. I think he enjoyed the control factor in these relationships. Made him feel big time. He liked to pick them up at the track. Go with them for a few weeks, then move on. But I got the drift and put it into my mental file on Craine.

"He was a loner. Didn't have too many friends. So I pretended to be very impressed whenever he talked about his job. He was really not allowed to do this, discussing his job which was a high level security position. So that became the first part of establishing trust – getting him to start opening up. Once that started happening, I knew I was on the right track."

"No pun intended."

"What? Oh – yes! Track. Racing....very good. Sense of humor. Very good."

"So he opened up - about working for the Kennedys?"

Yes. He told me many things, particularly about the reality of politics as he observed it. The way things were as opposed to the way it was written about or perceived my most Americans. He felt it was really a very dirty business – all about ego and power. Honesty, ethics, he would claim, forget it. It was all about their own private agendas. There was much he saw and overheard and there was some awfully dirty stuff going on. Especially with the women. The Kennedys did whatever they wanted. Whenever they wanted it. Which was good for me to hear because again – it pointed to a vulnerability. The leaders of his government were far from saints. Their morality was a joke. All in all, Craine was a man whose inner compass was becoming quite loose. But it was all below the surface. But that's recruiting, what we have to look for. Very rarely is it right out in the open. It was still just a light, good-natured friendship between us. Which is when I took it to the next level. Bonding."

"Bonding," I repeated.

"Absolutely crucial. In all cases. It varies, of course, how it's actually done – but there is usually a situation that is carefully prepared to cause the person considerable jeopardy or embarrassing misfortune unless there is a way out. And it is designed so that the agent is the one person he turns to for help in rescuing him from the dire circumstances. And that is exactly what happened with Craine."

"What did you do?"

"I arranged for him to be involved in a minor car accident –following one of our dinners after the track. It was all staged, somewhat messy, and his fault. I was in my car just behind. He was in a real panic, knew he had been drinking – too much, and that the cops would throw the book at him and that would be the end of everything. I told him to leave, that I had a cop friend and we'd handle it. There wasn't a lot of time to think and I made a strong case so he heeded my advice and left me to hopefully fix it."

"You actually did that?"

Yuri nodded. "It was relatively easy. Of course there was nothing to fix. Later I told Craine it had been a little sticky, but he didn't have anything to worry about."

"Didn't he want to know how you smoothed it over?"

"I told him it was taken care of, and the less he knew the better. Naturally, he was profoundly grateful."

"I should say.

"After that, trusting me like he did, he really opened up. We had, after all, bonded. He told me about the real stuff inside. The dream he had. What he really wanted. And that was to one day get into real estate. He was very keen on owning a hotel, maybe a chain. He really liked that idea, owning a really fine, prestigious hotel chain. So, with that in mind, I dangled a very alluring woman for him to meet, completely separate from me. Laura was very good, got right to him. She was a different woman from the others. But that was the point: I wanted Craine to start believing in himself more. What he was capable of. And there is no better ego booster than a woman. Catching one out of your league. And catching Laura gave him tremendous confidence. She was everything the others weren't – intelligent, sophisticated, caring and of course extremely beautiful. A very classy lady."

"But KGB."

"Yes. Trained and educated like any other agent. Quite common. We call them swallows. Men are so easily manipulated in this area. Pathetically. The right woman, with the right appeal, can be tremendously effective. And Laura was very good. She brought Craine to a new level of thinking about himself. A new level of confidence. He now believed he was capable of great things, thanks to Laura."

I shook my head, incredulous at the level of coercive subversion. Yuri smiled, reading my mind: "Yes, it seems incredible to you. But it's absolutely how they work. What they will do to get someone. Especially a Craine, in his position. Think of it – he s right there in that house with the President and Attorney General. In such a loose, casual atmosphere. When their guards were down, when they were playing. It would be an enormous coup to have someone inside. Under our control. So yes, we went to enormous lengths to catch him."

"It's staggering."

"Yes. But I assure you not uncommon. It's how the game is played from their side."

"So – Laura and Craine," I prompted him.

"Yes," he resumed, "very slowly she began making overtures about connections she had in real estate. Hotels, resorts. Just little things, people she knew who were in that line. So that Craine could see a connection. A

211

potential. A way to his dream – thru Laura. And how perfect because he was so infatuated. Then she got Craine to let her visit the Lawford house one night. She wanted to just see where the President and Attorney General came on their visits. Where all the parties were that Craine bragged about. It was strictly forbidden for Craine to allow such a thing. But Laura was very persuasive – and it became one more time Craine had crossed the line. Another violation of trust. We were establishing a pattern for him, wearing his reluctance down. I won't go into all the details, but once inside, Laura was able to smoothly indispose Craine so she might take some pictures and plant a bug."

"A surveillance bug?"

"Yes."

"Why?"

"I'm getting to that. The main thing is he let the snake into the garden. A few days later, Laura dangled the next bait. A friend had given her the inside track on a prime real estate deal. A hotel in Del Mar, on the beach. They drove down to check it out and Craine loved it. But it was a cash deal. $200,000. Obviously, he doesn't have that kind of funds at hand. But it's such an opportunity, he tells me over drinks after the track one evening. Where the hell could he get that kind of cash?"

Yuri paused. Looked at me. A faint smile. "This was the crossroad. Everything was coming together for him. He had a beautiful girl who was whispering all the right things in his ear. About the life they could share together. The power. The start of his empire. Together they'd conquer the world. But it had to start. And he truly believed it could begin with this deal."

"The dream."

"Staring him in the face, waiting for him to act. So he asks me if I know of any long shots to $200,000." And to this somewhat drunken, somewhat crazy but very real question I very carefully replied: `As a matter of fact, I just might'"

★★★★★

The waiter brought two beers and set them before us. We had adjourned across the street to one of the Promenade's many restaurants to continue over some lunch. We each took a sip. It was very cold and good. The place was pleasantly busy. Some warm Italian bread was set down for nibbling. Yuri continued.

212

So I mentioned to Craine about a certain acquaintance of mine. Not really a friend, although I believed and trusted him. And the acquaintance was in the unique position of having certain Soviet contacts that would pay handsomely for sensitive government documents."

"How did he react?"

"I remember his response quite clearly. He said - `describe handsomely`. And I answered probably enough to do his deal. He had a choice, but really it was already decided. I assured him it would be a one time arrangement only. He'd receive the cash, make his payment on the hotel, and within a reasonable time put in his resignation and get on with his new life. Take the money and run. He made some face about it, pretending to wrestle with his conscience, but he was in. From the start he was in. There was too much hypocrisy he'd witnessed with the government for him not to see this as an opportunity – and leave all the fuss about morality out."

"So he did it?"

"He did it, yes. I provided him with a camera and he was able finally to photograph some documents of the U.S. missile defense system. Because President Kennedy was only there several times a year, his direct opportunities were limited."

"Did he get his money?"

"Oh, yes. That's very important, establishing a pay-off link from us to him. The real estate deal fell through, but he still had the money and there would be other chances."

Our sandwiches arrived.

We ate.

"When," I asked between bites, "did you tell him?" Yuri looked at me. "When did you let the net fall?"

He nodded. "Not long. He was infuriated – especially about the bug, which he removed at once. But there was nothing he could do when it was all presented to him, the trap he was in. Everything was documented. He was sewn in tight. There was no way out, not without self-destructing."

"Cooperate or be crucified."

"Yes. But I tried to make him see it was still a two way street. He'd help us and we'd help him. He'd still be paid handsomely and promised him one day he'd get a clean exit from everything with the funds to underwrite a new life."

"He'd have his dream, but he'd pay the price."

"Yes."

"And he accepted?"

"More or less." The money tasted good. He was an animal in a cage and we said – be a good boy and one day we'll let you out of the cage."

"Light at the end of the tunnel."

"So to speak. But now, with Craine, he and I no longer met. I was his 'rezident' and basically became a transmitter of instructions from Central. We communicated by drops. That was the ad in the Times. I was letting him know the drop location to use. Fortunately, he never made it."

"Why fortunately?"

"I say that now in hindsight, though at the time in '62, I had only limited knowledge of Craine's activities."

"Was Laura gone?"

"Naturally. Her function was through. You see, the KGB is very careful to limit the number of people actually knowing any one operation. It protects against exposure. I was forwarded instructions for Craine without really knowing specifics. That's the drop location – passing instructions on."

"So you didn't know his association with Hoffa?"

"I knew this much," he lowered his voice, glancing discreetly at the closest adjoining tables. The eyes and ears nearby. An old habit, no doubt. "Craine was set up with Mr. H --- who believed Craine came from a sector of the CIA. Mr. K--- was the target."

I nodded slowly, trying to absorb this revelation.

"Beyond that, specifics, details, arrangements – I simply don't know. Except that it was Craine's final assignment. He was through and we were taking him out – as we'd promised."

"That explains the forged passport and ticket on him."

Yuri nodded. "But before leaving, he had a drop to make. Something highly important. I do not know what. My instructions were to forward it to Moscow immediately."

The film, I thought. "Why was he going to Cuba?"

"Temporary asylum."

I nodded. "Go back to what you said about it being fortunate the drop not going through. In hindsight."

"Whatever he was instructed to drop to me, it was undoubtedly meant to damage. Possibly destroy. The timing was so absolutely critical. It was only later I understood how monstrous it all was, how close it came to succeeding – and how devastating that success might have eventually been."

"What do you mean - timing?"

"What do you suppose the KGB wanted from all this?"

"Beyond damaging Kennedy, I'm not sure."

He smiled, finishing his beer. "I didn't either, not until late September. Early October of that year, 1962. Just a month after Marilyn. Think – what were the Soviets doing?"

I looked at him blankly.

"You said it yourself – where was Craine going --- ?"

"Cuba?"

He smiled, nodding: "Cuba. The Soviets were stockpiling the island with nuclear arms and missiles and before we knew it America and Russia were on the brink of nuclear war."

"The Cuban Missile Crisis," I said feeling the color drain from my face.

"Think of it," he continued, "why do you think Khrushchev had the gaul to believe his build-up of arms could go unchecked? It was so unprecedented. Putting missiles in your backyard. My God! What possessed him to think he could hope to get away with such blatant aggression? Because – he had something up his sleeve. So when he got down to the face off with Kennedy, he would reach up and lay that card down. And Monroe was that card. Kennedy had wavered during the Bay of Pigs and Krushchev was convinced he would back down again after applying the right pressure."

I studied him carefully – he was passionately sincere.

"It's amazing no one has noted the connection, the timing of it – her death and the Kennedy Missile crisis. Had Craine not been stopped, had the drop gone through, had Krushchev received his wild card – can you imagine how different that face off would have been? He was so profoundly vulnerable at a time of such enormous historic consequences."

"They would really, actually do that?"

He smiled at my naiveté. "Do you really think for one moment the KGB care about etiquette? Do you think Krushchev felt for Kennedy's right to privacy – like your journalists? Do you think they mattered about any unwritten code of diplomacy? No. Of course not. Dear boy, we are talking about war. The Cold War. A battle of ideologies. All that mattered was getting those missiles onto Cuba – into the Western Hemisphere. And if that meant helping along the inevitable demise of one drunken, pill-popping, capitalist movie star and embarrassing the President – well, fine!"

I looked at him with sunken, bewildered eyes: "The casualties of war."

"Nothing more. Look – if nothing else, the decades of the 60's and 70's revealed what men in government, men of place and power are capable of doing. Executions, hits, break-ins, assassinations, cover-ups – its an endless list of brutal, ruthless, covert machinations."

He stared at me, his eyes shimmering with an energy to make me feel the truth of his words.

"I am old. And the older I get, the more it is true – that truth is indeed stranger than fiction. I have no reason to lie. I just want someone to understand. The way it is. The way it was. When you get to be my age not so much matters. But the truth does. The truth matters. Before I check out, it's something to at least attempt to get right." He stood up, placing his napkin down. "Think about it for a moment while I relieve myself of this wonderful beer we've been drinking."

I did.

Five minutes went by and no sign of him. I began to wonder. Maybe old people take longer. Maybe he had to make a phone call as well.

Another five minutes. Still nothing. I was concerned now. The waiter asked about dessert. No thanks. Just the check.

Three minutes later it arrived with a note. Handwritten. Single piece of paper. From Yuri. It read:

I must go. Sorry to leave like this.
But it's best. Please try and believe
What I have related. The U.S. tried
Assassinating Castro with the mob. Is
It any different for the KGB to use
Hoffa to hush Kennedy when they
Wanted desperately to have their
Missiles in Cuba. Wouldn't it have
Made a perfect bargaining chip – had
They been able to use it?

Fortunately, they weren't. That word
Again. But I do, finally, feel
Fortunate in now getting the chance
To tell this. It is a small gesture
To your country for the freedom

216

they have granted me for the last
half of my life. Use what you can for
the book. Just don't count on my
joining you at any book signings.
Joke – ha, ha.

Poor Marilyn. The ultimate, tragic
victim. So very sad, caught like that.

I miss Kennedy. He had faults but he
was a good president. More than other
world leaders, he was looking at the big
picture – at world unity. And remember,
too, who assassinated him.

Far-fetched? No, my friend. Please
believe me. And good luck with the
book. It's time people knew. And
more, it's time to understand.

Good by,

Yuri.

I paid and walked over to the Palisades. I looked down. There across the street, along PCH, fronting the beach – stood the old Lawford house. I wondered about many things. I read Yuri's note again, memorizing it as best I could. Then threw it out, over the edge – toward the ocean.

✳ ✳ ✳ ✳ ✳

That night.

Following dinner and relating everything to Zhen, the whole amazing account by Yuri. We were outside, on our deck, enjoying coffees and the warm summer evening.

A final thought from Zhen: "Do you suppose," she began, "it's possible Beach was in any way – somehow involved down there in Cuba, or wherever he was after landing in Mexico – in any of the Cuban Missile Crisis?"

"Like staying on the payroll and saving Kennedy's ass once more?"

217

"Yeah. Something like that."

Interesting question.

Mr. Beach...Lou... wherever you are – would you care to respond?